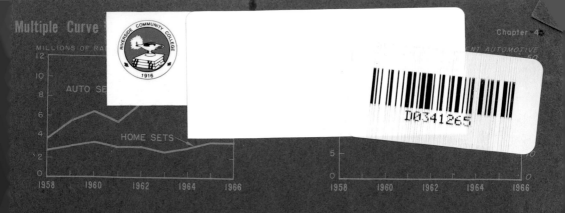

Chapter 4

MILLIONS OF RADIOS
12
10
8
6
4
2
0

AUTO SETS

HOME SETS

1958 1960 1962 1964 1966

PERCENT AUTOMOTIVE
50

5

0

1958 1960 1962 1964 1966

D0341265

Logarithm

Chapter 4

MILLIONS OF RADIOS
25
20
15
10

PRO

1958 1960

Subdivided Surface

Chapter 5

Battery

1964 1966

Subdivided Column

MILLIONS OF RADIOS
25

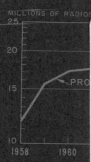
Auto
Portable Battery
Home

20
15
10
5
0

1958 1960

Chapter 7

PERCENT AUTOMOTIVE
50

Pie or Sector

PERCENT
AU

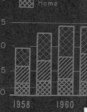
32
68

1961

60

Other

Chapter 10

BATTERY RADIOS

omitted on charts

Practical
Charting
Techniques

Practical Charting Techniques

Mary Eleanor Spear

Graphic Analyst and Lecturer
Formerly Visual Information Specialist,
Bureau of Labor Statistics, United States
Department of Labor, and Lecturer,
The American University, Washington, D.C.

McGRAW-HILL BOOK COMPANY

New York   St. Louis   San Francisco   London
Sydney   Toronto   Mexico   Panama

*A small proportion of the text and illustrations in
this book has been derived or adapted from the author's
previous work,* Charting Statistics *(McGraw-Hill, 1952).*

60010

1234567890 MAMM 754321069

Preface

The response to a visual presentation will determine its value. As maximum response is the objective, the design of a visual for a nontechnical audience should be guided by the fundamental rule *keep it simple*. *Practical Charting Techniques* aims to meet this criterion by explaining the principles of charting and illustrating standard methods and forms of graphic presentation with uncomplicated charts and text.

This book will serve as a practical manual for those who make, use, or view charts, maps, and diagrams. It shows that careful planning and close collaboration between the communicator, the graphic analyst, and the draftsman give the best results, and details their responsibilities from the conception of the visual to its final realization. It also points out the need for the communicator to be familiar with his visuals and his equipment before giving a presentation.

The subject matter of the charts covers a wide range and should be of interest to those in business, management, government, advertising, education, and all who are concerned with visualizing economic and statistical data. Judicious treatment of artwork is illustrated, and examples of illusions that may result in *cheating by charting* are given. This section will interest both the maker and the viewer of charts; they will become more aware of the distortions and optical illusions that can be created, intentionally or unintentionally, in designing a visual. It also reveals how these illusions may be used to advantage in displays and exhibits.

Some of the topics discussed in the text and shown in the 276 illustrations are: illustrating a nonstatistical written report, charting and designing pictographs, changing a statistical analysis into a popular presentation, constructing charts showing the organization of businesses, industries, and governments, using maps as a basis for an economic survey, preparing visuals for reproduction or projection, planning color schemes, and using panels and kits for displays.

Shortcuts to layouts and the practical use of commercial materials are illustrated at the point where the problem arises. Simple formulas and tables on ratios, diameters, and square and cube roots are included to be used in determining the size of layouts or the size of graphic symbols. Other tables show how data should be prepared for drafting-room plotting, how indexes are obtained for selected base years, and why particular types of charts are suited to certain kinds of data. The illustrations on the endpapers give different interpretations and analyses based on a single table of data. They show how important it is to know the various types of charts and their particular uses. As in my book *Charting Statistics* (from which a small proportion of the text and illustrations has been derived), this manual not only presents the standard types of charts but adds numerous graphic layouts and techniques that are relevant to a specific objective or the needs of a specific audience.

Unless otherwise noted the illustrations were made by the author. Many of these originally appeared in technical, statistical, and economic books, magazine articles, reports of study committees, and in government publications. They were selected from problems encountered during years of analyzing and presenting data for the National Bureau of Standards, the Bureau of Labor Statistics of the United States Labor Department, the Natural Resources Division of the Treasury Department, and on assignments for the Bureau of the Budget of the Executive Office of the President, the White House, the Department of Defense, the Selective Service System, other federal agencies, Senate and House committees, congressmen, labor unions, business groups, associations, and private individuals. The author's other experiences with graphic presentation include teaching college students and military groups, conducting workshops and trainee sessions, lecturing at conferences, and teaching special students in her own studio.

The author wishes to express her appreciation to Dr. Isaac Paul Salto, economist, formerly with the International Institute of Agriculture, Rome, Italy, and the Food and Agriculture Organization of the United Nations, for his translation of Italian text and for review; to Frederick F. Otto, Director of Continuing Education, Hagerstown Junior College, Maryland, for reviewing material on home rule from the final report of the Washington County Study Commission; to Mrs. Sylvia Q. Schaff, illustrator, for her assistance in the preparation of the charts and time given assembling data; and to those organizations and firms who granted permission for the use of their data, photographs, and illustrative materials.

Mary E. Spear

List of Figures

List of Tables

Contents

ONE Graphic Presentation 1

Popular Graphic Representation. Use of Visuals; Designing the Chart. Selecting the Type of Chart. The Importance of Collaboration. The Communicator. The Graphic Analyst. The Draftsman. The Written Report. Evaluation.

TWO Planning the Chart 19

Results of No Planning. Planning the Working Area. Proportioning Layouts. Methods for Determining Size. Proportion by Ratio. Enlarging and Reducing by Angles. Projecting a Diagonal. The Planned Layout. The Standard Trend Chart. Lettering the Main Title. The Subtitle. The Trends. Component Chart Labels. The Grids. The Vertical Grid Label. The Horizontal Grid Label. Scale Captions. Scale Unit. Notes and Sources. Template Lettering Guide. Fototype. Misspelled Words. Reversing Characters. Wording for Charts. Weight of

Lines. The Curve Line. The Border. The Base Line. Grid Lines. Ticks. Arrows. Constructing Wide Trend Lines. Tapes for Trends. Patterned Tapes. Crosshatching and Shading Films. Commercial Crosshatch Patterns. Hand Crosshatching. Color and Tint Shading. The Airbrush. Shading Sheets. Stylizing.

ONE

Graphic Presentation

Graphic presentation is the recognized medium for visually expressing statistical data and economic facts for popular appeal. Charts add a dimension to the meaning of words of a communicator whether the message is spoken or written.

The increasing emphasis on technical, scientific, and social developments has opened new areas in visual media and produced an expanded mass-communication need throughout the world.

Industrial, commercial, financial, governmental, educational, and all scientific fields of technology are depending more on communicating knowledge and ideas through some form of audio or visual outlet.

POPULAR GRAPHIC REPRESENTATION

Each field has its own concept of graphic methods and standards of presentation and its own identifying codes, nomenclatures, or symbols. Each has its own language and calls for specialization. But there is a time and a place when all fields have a need to

1

present their progress, development, results, or plans in graphic formats that are meaningful and retentive to either a specific or a general audience. It is here that charting of quantitative or qualitative data can perform its diversified functions. Here, any audience level can be reached by depicting the message in *popular* presentations. And here, the byword of charting "Keep It Simple" applies to all visual presentations.

USE OF VISUALS

Statistical charts, maps, pictograms, diagrams, and other visual illustrations are appearing more often in newspapers, magazines, and annual reports, on television, and at public hearings and closed meetings. In fact they *should* appear wherever a commutable idea can be put into an informative visual presentation.

With the numerous types of charts to choose from and the various methods of presenting them, thorough analyzing of data and careful planning of layouts are essential. Good graphic presentation has only one interpretation.

DESIGNING THE CHART

Correctly designed charts should make:
1. A *statistical fact* more graphically explicit
2. A *point of view* more significantly emphasized
3. An economic *situation* more clearly visualized

The viewer's first impression upon seeing the chart is vital. Attract him, and you can hold him if your message is clear and concise. Do not clutter up the chart. Trying to tell too much will only confuse the story.

SELECTING THE TYPE OF CHART

Knowing all types of charts and their specific function is essential. Those based on *graphic form* are the line, surface, column, bar, pie or sector, and map charts. Charts based on *scale arrangement* are the multiple-time, multiple-amount, and logarithmic (see inside front and back covers).

While each type of chart has a basic format for its need, flexibility of rules on occasion may be necessary. For example, if the data for a chart are for one item over a consecutive period of time and plottings for individual years are to be stressed, a *column* chart would be the first choice. But, assuming that the given space for the chart is higher than it is wide, a more readable layout would be a *bar* chart format. A *line* chart would accent the trend, not the years (see charts in Fig. 1-1).

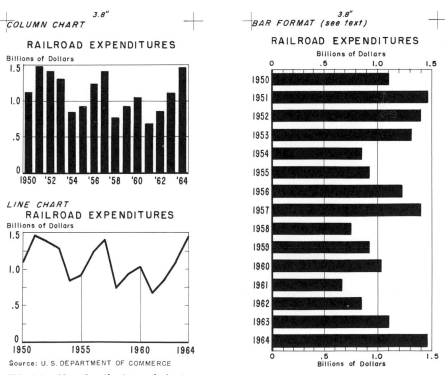

FIG. 1-1 Choosing the type of chart.

THE IMPORTANCE OF COLLABORATION

Because there are numerous types of charts to meet different situations and a wide choice of media with which to present them, it is advisable that the *communicator,* the *graphic analyst,* and the *draftsman* collaborate (see Fig. 1-2).

This could involve one, two, or more persons, as the communicator may be familiar with the purposes of various types of charts and media, which is part of the duties of the graphic analyst. He may even be skilled in drafting. But no matter how many take part in the preparation of the visuals, there are fundamental steps that should be considered to achieve effective results.

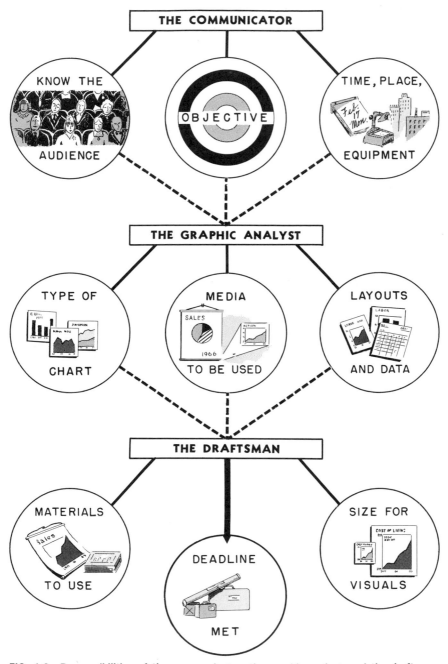

FIG. 1-2 Responsibilities of the communicator, the graphic analyst, and the draftsman.

THE COMMUNICATOR

In order that the *communicator* may know what to say, how to present it, and when to prepare it, he must be informed on:

1. *The size and composition of his audience.* Knowing the size of the audience and how familiar they are with the subject will help the communicator render his speech more meaningful. He should be sure of his facts. If it is a controversial subject, he should have supporting evidence that will back up his point of view. This is where well-planned charts can make a graphic impact.

2. *The objective of the meeting.* It is essential that the communicator know why he was called on to speak—what particular aspect in his vocation or avocation the audience is interested in. This enables him to draw on his experience to their advantage.

3. *The time, place, and available equipment.* Knowing the date of the speech and the time allotted him will enable him to plan the length of his speech and the number of visuals he can handle.

He should be told not just the place where the meeting will be held, but what the physical surroundings will be—whether he will be making his presentation at floor level, on a platform, or around a conference table. This will help him select his visual media for presentation.

He should know the type of available visual equipment, that is, the type of projector, easel, microphone, lectern, etc., and if an operator or assistant will be on hand.

This information the communicator passes on to the *graphic analyst,* who is thoroughly familiar with all types of graphic presentations and media and knows which types will best emphasize the objective of the message.

THE GRAPHIC ANALYST

The *graphic analyst* advises the communicator on:

1. *The type of chart.* It is essential that the right *type* of chart be selected to emphasize the message. This requires thorough analysis of the data and situation to be met. For example, at a sales meeting, a general sales picture is to be shown from 1950 through 1965 with emphasis on individual years of nondurable sales (see Fig. 1-3). This is depicted by using the subdivided-column chart which identifies the *years* readily. The nondurable-goods data are plotted at the bottom of the column where they are more easily read from the zero line.

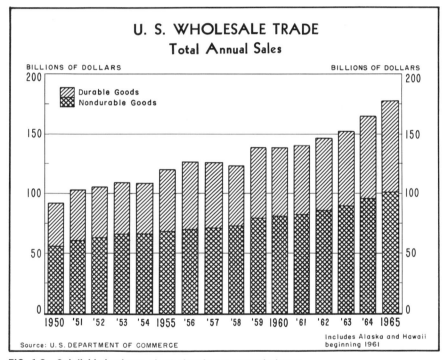

FIG. 1-3 Subdivided-column chart showing a general picture.

If, however, the message called for the direct comparison of the *trends* of durable and nondurable sales, a multiple-line chart would be more explicit (see Fig. 1-4).

2. *The choice of media.* The size of the audience and the equipment available are deciding factors concerning the type of media to be used. Equipment should be in good working condition,

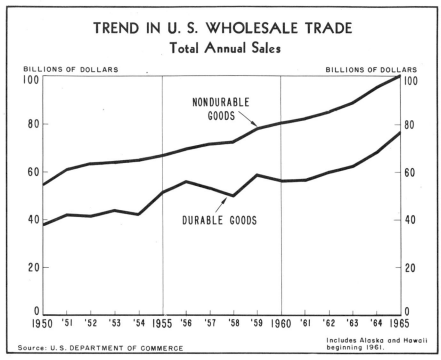

FIG. 1-4   Multiple-line chart showing trends.

and charts should be carefully checked for content and sequence.

A turnover chart book, as in Fig. 1–5, or separate charts about 15 by 20 in. can be used for sales presentations, staff meetings, executive briefings, and similar *small groups*. The charts may be passed around for general discussions. Having discussion breaks during an informal session has a more lasting impression than do questions later on. Answers are more meaningful at the time of presentation.

FIG. 1-5   Turnover chart book for small groups.

In lecturing before trainee groups or foreign students, I find it advantageous for them to have a brief outline of the talk accompanied by copies of the charts to be shown. When possible, small samples of shading sheets, tapes, adhesive lettering, Fototype, and other materials used—along with demonstrations of·mechanical devices—will help them more readily understand and identify these visual media by their trade names. Several art and drafting companies have samples of their materials available upon request.

For showing transparencies to a small group, there are illuminated viewers, such as the Tecnilite (see Fig. 1-6) which comes in a compact luggage case. This case serves as an easel for displaying transparencies about 7 by 10 in.

The speaker may write or draw at will, with grease pencils or colored acetate markers, directly on the transparencies or sheets of clear acetate.

FIG. 1-6 Tecnilite viewer for transparencies. (Tecnifax Division, The Plastic Coating Corp.)

Large groups call for various types of projections; transparencies, films, filmstrips, technamations, slides, etc. Easel or wall charts should be at least 30 by 40 in. Lettering should be kept at a minimum and bold enough to be read at a distance.

Supplying your own equipment and experienced operator is more reliable, but not always feasible. Slides call for cuing an operator, while projectuals on an overhead machine may be handled by an operator or the speaker. Cuing an operator is done by a system of signals or by means of a prepared script. The cued script is not always practicable, as the speaker may want to add a new point or to adjust his pace to meet the response of the audience. This timing of slides can be controlled by the communicator if the projector is a remote control model.

The overhead projector has an advantage over the slide projector, as the overhead model allows the speaker to have full control over his projectuals. The machine is set up in the front of the room and close to the screen. The speaker sits facing the audience while the image is projected over his shoulder. He can

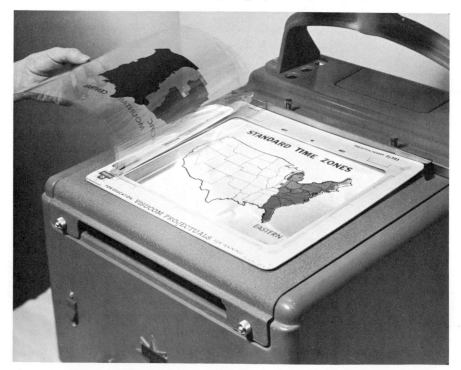

FIG. 1-7   Hinging overlays in sequence. (Tecnifax Division, The Plastic Coating Corp.)

set his own pace, change the sequence of the transparencies, and write or draw with special markers on the acetate visuals as the need arises.

Overlays can build up a composite image on transparent projectuals. These overlays are attached with hinges at one side of the projectual when following a sequence (see Fig. 1-7) or on different edges if the sequence is varied (see Fig. 1-8).

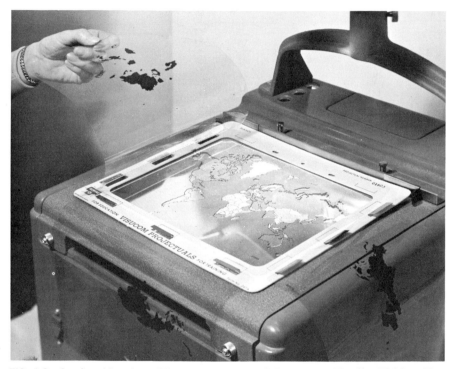

FIG. 1-8   Overlays hinged on different edges for varied sequence. (Tecnifax Division, The Plastic Coating Corp.)

3. *The preparation of rough layouts and data.* The graphic analyst should check and see that the rough layouts for the draftsman are complete in all wording and that the scales are inclusive for the data. Often a draftsman will accept a rough layout, only to find that one or two figures in the basic table are above the scale designated on the sketch.

Few drafting rooms have calculating machines, and any additions, averages, totals, indexes, etc., needed for plotting the charts should be computed before presenting the data. For example, cumulations for plotting a subdivided-surface chart should be added so that it may be plotted directly from a table without the draftsman having to stop and add each amount (see Fig. 1-9 and Tables 1-1*A* and 1-1*B*). This is a time-saver in the drafting room and an accuracy check for the analyst.

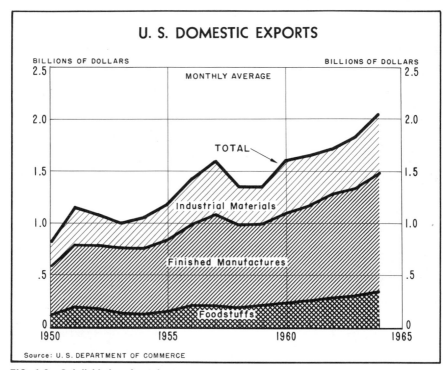

FIG. 1-9   Subdivided-surface chart.

TABLE 1-1A   *United States Domestic Exports (Millions of Dollars)*
Original table

Year	Foodstuffs	Finished manufactures	Industrial materials	Total exports
1950	116	455	251	822
1951	190	616	345	1,151
1952	175	612	300	1,088
1953	143	614	254	1,012
1954	131	620	310	1,060
1955	162	667	351	1,180
1956	216	775	441	1,432
1957	208	872	530	1,611
1958	198	784	368	1,351
1959	210	776	366	1,352
1960	230	877	510	1,617
1961	254	919	486	1,659
1962	281	1,002	440	1,723
1963	314	1,031	494	1,839
1964	348	1,150	566	2,064

Note: Total figures may vary in last digit due to rounding in original data.
SOURCE: U.S. Department of Commerce, Bureau of International Commerce.

TABLE 1-1B   *United States Domestic Exports (Millions of Dollars)*
Table 1-1A cumulated for plotting Fig. 1-9

Year	Foodstuffs	+	Finished manufactures	+	Industrial materials	=	Total exports
1950	116		571				822
1951	190		806				1,151
1952	175		787				1,087
1953	143		757				1,011
1954	131		751				1,061
1955	162		829				1,180
1956	216		991				1,432
1957	208		1,080				1,610
1958	198		982				1,350
1959	210		986				1,352
1960	230		1,107				1,617
1961	254		1,173				1,659
1962	281		1,283				1,723
1963	314		1,345				1,839
1964	348		1,498				2,064

Note: Total figures may vary in last digit due to rounding in original data.
SOURCE: U.S. Department of Commerce, Bureau of International Commerce.

THE DRAFTSMAN

It is important that the graphic analyst give the *draftsman* the background on the use of the visuals, the media to be employed, and the date of the project. If the draftsman has had an elementary course in statistics, he will have a better understanding of the charts assigned him.

With the basic facts on hand, the draftsman will know:

1. *What materials to use.* Knowing whether slides, wall charts, or turnover charts are to be used, the draftsman knows definitely what materials should go into the making of each visual. He should keep the analyst informed about any new materials or equipment that have been added to his division, such as acetate for overlays (see Fig. 1-10) or an airbrush and accessories. New equipment will not only give the analyst an opportunity to vary the aspect of the visuals but will progressively improve the output and results of the drafting room.

2. *What size to make the visuals.* Having a clear understanding of the project, the draftsman can determine the sizes of the visuals and proportion them to the different media to be used.

Careful planning of the size of lettering, weight of lines, design of shading, or selection of colors will find its reward in an eye-catching and interest-holding project.

3. *The final date.* The deadline of the project, of course, tells the draftsman how much time he can spend on the job. Unfortunately he is usually the last one to know about the amount of work to be done. Therefore, the more shortcuts the draftsman knows or can invent to cut down the amount of time normally needed for a bang-up job, the more valuable he is to the graphic analyst and communicator. It is to their advantage to see that the data and layouts get into the drafting room as soon as possible.

Many times the final data are not available until the last moment. In that case, give the draftsman an estimated figure in order that adequate scale allowance may be made on the chart. In the meantime he can be planning the style of lettering, the materials, and the layout for the project.

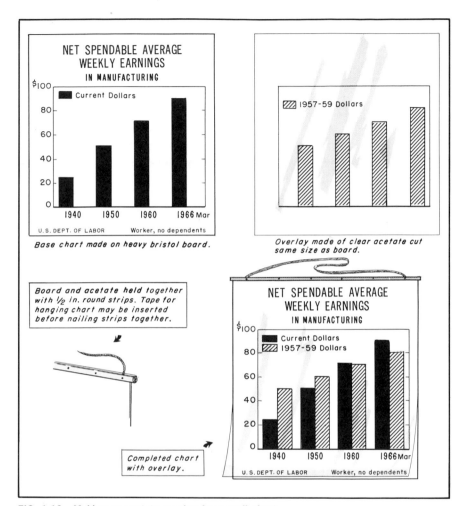

FIG. 1-10   Making an acetate overlay for a wall chart.

THE WRITTEN REPORT

As a rule, when a report, study, or any text is being written, the author has in mind certain charts or illustrations that will clarify points of his objective visually. Though his sketch may not be the correct type of chart, it will serve as a reminder that here would be a good place to pause visually.

These sketch memos can later be reviewed for their value in enhancing or simplifying a point to be made. Suggestions from the graphic analyst regarding the type of chart can be considered. Reproduction problems involving page layout and materials to be used can be handled by the draftsman.

EVALUATION

No matter what purpose a chart is to serve, evaluate it.

1. Does the type of chart selected give a comprehensive picture of the message?

2. Does the chart as a whole accurately present the facts?

3. Does the size of the chart and visual media used satisfy all audience or reader requirements?

4. Is the chart visually balanced for display use or for the printed page?

5. Is the layout well proportioned and the style of lettering in harmony?

6. Do the materials meet all projection and reproduction requirements?

7. Is the planned idea an effective visual tool?

If the chart does not seem to hit the target, drop it. If there is time to make another that will hit the bull's eye, make it.

FIG. 1-11   The message must get across.

TWO

Planning the Chart

Before any planning of the original layout of a chart is started, be certain that:

1. The *data* have been carefully analyzed.
2. The *objective* of the message has been determined.
3. The most effective *type* of chart has been selected to depict that message.
4. The best *visual device* has been chosen to display it.

Only then can it be known what materials are most suitable to use and what size chart layout, lettering, and weight of lines should be drafted.

RESULTS OF NO PLANNING

"What's the matter with our charts?" This question has been asked many times. In most cases the correct type of chart has been selected, but no thought has been given to visualizing the chart as a balanced unit. Thus, the impact of its objective has been lost.

19

The three charts in Fig. 2-1 were made similar in *structure* to charts from various publications. All lettering was made the same size and weight as carried on these selected charts. Basically there is nothing the matter with the charts that could not be remedied by more careful *planning* of the layout, *size* of lettering, *weight* of line work, and *emphasis* of the message.

Chart 1 in Fig. 2-1 is much too light in weight of line work and lettering to be effective. It needs more grid to be read properly. And what is the unit of measure? There is no labeled base line. Without ticks or stubs the years are difficult to identify. The source and notes should be the smallest lettering, but in this case they appear next in size to the title and subtitle of the chart. Arrows running horizontally are not as effective as those drafted at approximately right angles to the trend lines.

In chart 2, Fig. 2-1, the shading patterns were poorly chosen. While the patterns are different in design, there is not enough contrast in their *value* to make the bands visually striking.

Since we read from left to right in our language, a pattern with a definite directional slope should be slanted to the right. This tends to carry the eye forward with the movement of the trend. Therefore, the diagonal in stratum *C* would be more progressive if the pattern were sloped to the right.

Also, in the selection of the hachures on the original chart, allowance was not made for the closing up of the patterns when the chart was reduced in reproduction. This resulted in the chart appearing too heavy in visual balance for the accompanying text.

The confusion in chart 3, Fig. 2-1, is caused by *busy patterns* of the tapes and the labeling of the trends. In this chart, narrower tapes and use of standard dot-and-dash patterns instead of diagonals would help attain a clearer reading (see tape patterns in Fig. 2-18).

The wedge-shaped symbols, identifying the trends, drafted at different angles add to the confusion.

The foregoing comments were primarily made to call attention to the fact that so-called little things can detract from the effectiveness of a good presentation.

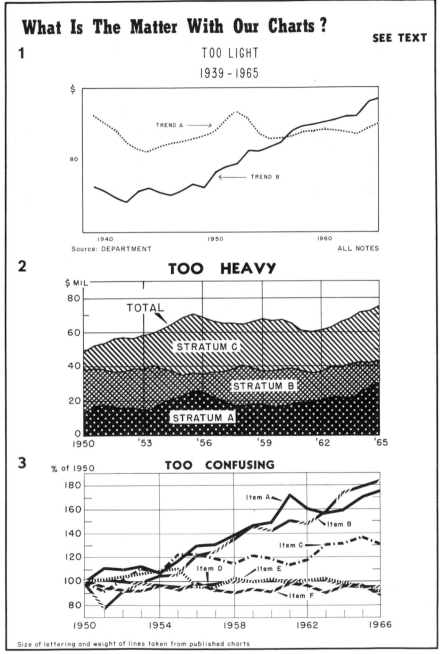

What Is The Matter With Our Charts?

SEE TEXT

1 TOO LIGHT

1939 - 1965

TREND A →

← TREND B

Source: DEPARTMENT   ALL NOTES

2 TOO HEAVY

TOTAL

STRATUM C

STRATUM B

STRATUM A

3 TOO CONFUSING

% of 1950

Item A

Item B

Item C

Item D   Item E

Item F

Size of lettering and weight of lines taken from published charts

FIG. 2-1   Results of no planning.

PLANNING THE WORKING AREA

When all the basic facts on the visual are in hand, the first step to take is to lay out the frame for the working area.

Charts to be reproduced for publication in books, reports, or articles are seldom made the actual size of the allotted space. They should be drafted in proportion to the space in a working area large enough to construct the chart with ease. This enlarged layout will appear sharper and neater when reduced, as slight deficiencies in the line work and lettering are minimized.

Make the working drawing two to three times the reduced area, depending upon the detail involved in the type of chart selected. The majority of charts drafted in this book were laid out twice the size of the printed charts. Those whose trends ran over a long period of time and the larger maps were three times their reproduced size.

PROPORTIONING LAYOUTS

When proportioning the working area for a full-page chart, consider whether the chart will run horizontally or vertically on the page. If the printer is to run in a title or a legend at the top or bottom of the chart, allow room for this in the layout.

A title lettered by the draftsman has a more balanced and finished appearance than one set up in type underneath the chart. Then too, with a drafted title there is no danger of mistaking the identity of a graph later on, and it will always be ready for another use.

METHODS FOR DETERMINING SIZE

There are several methods of enlarging and reducing when determining a proportional size. Some prefer to do it mathematically; others, having a T square, triangles, and decimal or engineer's scale at hand, find it quicker by the line-extension method.

PROPORTION BY RATIO

Let us assume that the allotted space for the printed chart is 5.3 in. wide and 4 in. high. The draftsman wishes to draw in a working area 12 in. wide.

The *height* of the original working area may be determined by ratio as follows:

5.3 in. (width) : 4 in. (height) : : 12 in. (known width) : X (height)

$$\frac{4 \times 12}{5.3} = \frac{48}{5.3} = 9.0 \text{ in. (height for working area)}$$

Or, the *width* of the original working area may be determined when the height, 9.0 in., is known as follows:

4 in. (height) : 5.3 in. (width) : : 9 in. (known height) : X (width)

$$\frac{5.3 \times 9}{4} = \frac{47.7}{4} = 12 \text{ in. (width for working area)}$$

Thus the working area drawn 9 by 12 in. will reduce to the area originally allotted to the chart (see Fig. 2-2).

ENLARGING AND REDUCING BY ANGLES

Part 2 in Fig. 2-2 illustrates how to find the new width or height of a layout by the use of angles.

Measure the *original* width of the layout on line *AB*. Using a 30°-60° triangle, or any convenient angle, draw line *AC* the length of the *original* height. Connect *BC*.

For a *reduction* of the layout:

1. When the reduced *width* is known, measure this new width *Ab* on line *AB*. From *b* draw a line parallel to *BC* cutting line *AC* at *c*. The length of the line *Ac* will be the reduced height.

2. When the reduced *height* is given, measure this new height *Ac* on line *AC*. From *c* draw a line parallel to *BC* cutting line *AB* at *b*. The length of line *Ab* will be the reduced width.

For an *enlargement* of the layout, extend the original lines *AB* and *AC* to the known new width or height and proceed with the method above.

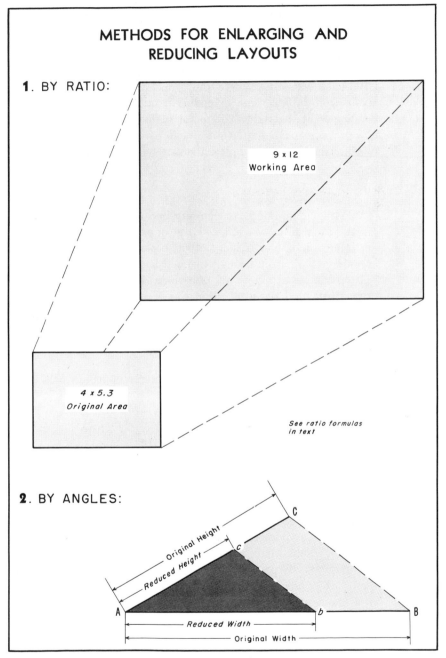

FIG. 2-2   Enlarging and reducing by ratio and angles.

PROJECTING A DIAGONAL

Part 1, Fig. 2-3, illustrates a simple method of keeping areas in proportion when enlarging. Lay out the given size. Extend the base line to the right to the desired new length. Erect a perpendicular at each end of this line. Draw a diagonal through the original layout from left to right, extending it until it intersects the perpendicular at the right. This point of intersection will give the new proportional height. A line drawn parallel to the base through this intersection will complete the new working area of the chart.

THE PLANNED LAYOUT

When a planned layout is necessary, because charts or illustrations and text are wanted on a lettered page or exhibit without a paste-up job, follow the line-extension method in part 2, Fig. 2-3. This shows an enlargement from a small planned layout.

1. In the upper left corner of a piece of bristol board place the original planned layout at point A.

2. From A measure down the desired height for the enlargement and draw the line AB.

3. Extend a horizontal line from B across the board to the right. This is the bottom of the enlargement.

4. Draw a line from A parallel to line B; this will be the top of the new layout.

5. Next, run a diagonal from A through the lower right corner of the small original planned layout until it cuts line B at C. This gives the proportional width of the *new layout*.

6. Erecting a perpendicular at C, cutting line A at D, completes the enlarged working area.

To position the charts or illustrations in this area, extend all vertical and horizontal lines by drawing light dashed lines to the right and bottom edges of the original layout, forming points 1, 2, 3, 4, etc. Using A as a point of origin, draw diagonals through these points, extending them to the right and bottom edges of the enlarged working area. By projecting perpendicular and horizontal lines at these last points of intersection (1_1, 2_1, 3_1, 4_1, etc.), the height, width, and position of the different parts of the enlarged layout are determined.

Thus in part 2, Fig. 2–3, points 1-1_1, 2-2_1, 3-3_1, 4-4_1, etc., indicate corresponding positions. By extending and intersecting

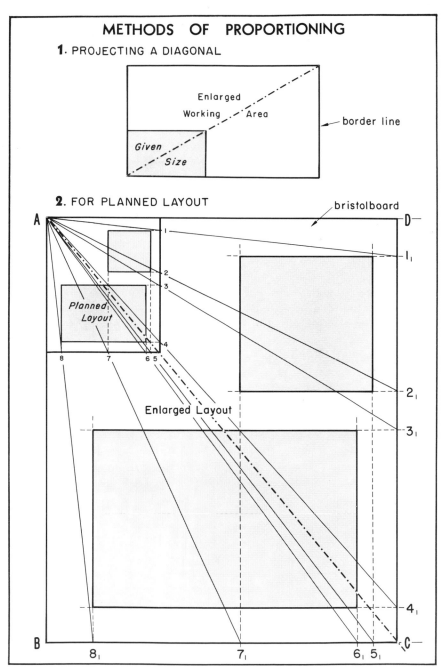

METHODS OF PROPORTIONING

1. PROJECTING A DIAGONAL

Enlarged
Working   Area

Given
Size

border line

2. FOR PLANNED LAYOUT

bristolboard

Planned
Layout

Enlarged Layout

FIG. 2-3   Proportioning a planned layout.

lines from the *prime* points, as shown in the diagram, the enlarge-ment will reduce to the original planned arrangement.

All preliminary layout drawing should be in light pencil or blue line work.

THE STANDARD TREND CHART

For those charts that are more or less routine, that is, regularly published or of uniform size for a chart room or meeting, standard layouts can be established and approved by all concerned. Used as a pattern in the drafting room, they will cut down the time and speed up work on such charts. Size of lettering and weight of lines can be referred to quickly. They will also show how, with possible slight changes, they may be adapted to another problem.

Lettering guides were used for all lettering in Fig. 2-4. This basic trend chart was made primarily to identify its components and to give their relative importance by comparing the lettering sizes and weight of lines. The lettering ranges from the title, made with Leroy template No. 240 and No. 3 pen, to the note and source, made with a No. 100 template and No. 00 pen. The weight of lines ranges from the heaviest—*a*, the trend line—to the lightest—*f*, the ticks or stubs.

This example chart, which has been reduced one-half its original size, does not mean that all charts should carry this size lettering or weight of lines. It serves to show only the relation of one element to another. Each chart has its own problems in balance and its own message to stress. Longer titles, curve labels, trend movements, scales, and type and size of chart will all call for specific considera-tion and planning to reach a harmonious composition of compo-nents.

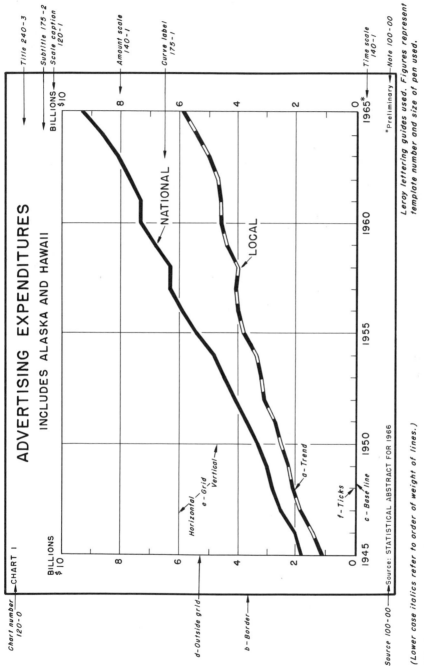

FIG. 2-4 Components of a standard trend chart. (Chart reduced one half.)

LETTERING THE MAIN TITLE

The main title has the most prominent lettering. It should be brief but at the same time clearly convey the subject of the graph. The wording, however, should change to suit the audience. "Advertising Expenditures" serves a formal need, but "Advertising Expenditures Steadily Advance" or "Advertising Expenditures Are at an All-time High" suits a more popular presentation. Use wording to fit the occasion.

The title is usually centered on the chart, but leave it to the prerogative of the layout man to position it for the best visual balance.

THE SUBTITLE

The subtitle supports the main title and carries essential details, such as dates, index base, or limits of coverage. It should be brief and used only to ensure clearness of subject. Do not depend on the text of the article or report to give basic information about your chart. The chart itself should include the major facts.

THE TRENDS

The curve or trend labels identify the plotted data. On a multiple-trend chart, where several trends intersect, avoid labeling them where they cross, as it is not immediately clear to which trend the labels refer.

If the trends are plotted so close together that it is difficult to label them directly, a legend or key must be carried. As a rule, each line is drafted in a different dash-and/or-dot symbol. The pattern that represents each trend would be labeled in the legend.

In Fig. 2-5, the two larger-amount trends were labeled directly, while the four lower trends were identified in the legend by *a*, *b*, *c*, and *d*. Only trend *c* was made a symbol line, as a series of dot-and-dash patterns for the four trends would have proved too difficult to interpret.

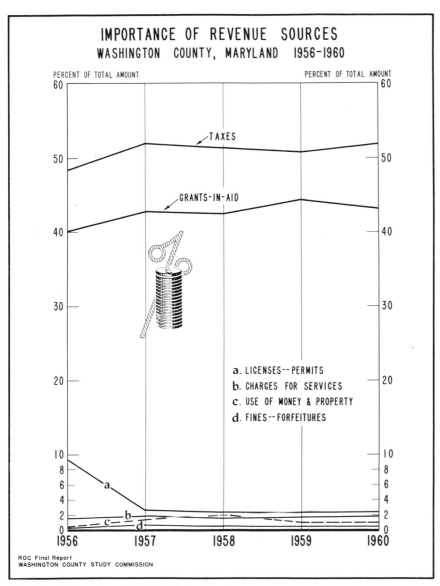

IMPORTANCE OF REVENUE SOURCES
WASHINGTON COUNTY, MARYLAND 1956-1960

PERCENT OF TOTAL AMOUNT

PERCENT OF TOTAL AMOUNT

TAXES

GRANTS-IN-AID

a. LICENSES--PERMITS
b. CHARGES FOR SERVICES
c. USE OF MONEY & PROPERTY
d. FINES--FORFEITURES

ROC Final Report
WASHINGTON COUNTY STUDY COMMISSION

FIG. 2-5   Using a legend for identifying trends.

COMPONENT CHART LABELS

Component-bar and -column charts usually carry a legend identifying each segment (see Fig. 1-3), while subdivided-surface charts are labeled directly in the patterned areas (see Fig. 5-7).

THE GRIDS

Labeling of the grid is the next size lettering to be considered. Lettering should be distinctly legible, and there should be labels only where they are essential for ease in reading the graph. Too many scale numerals and too much grid tend to be confusing (see Fig. 2-6).

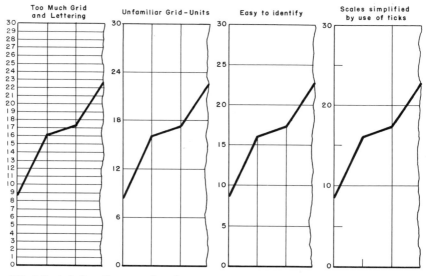

FIG. 2-6   Labeling the amount scale.

THE VERTICAL GRID LABEL

In labeling the units of the vertical amount scale, letter the numerals directly opposite the grids they represent. A grid should be divided into units of 1, 2, and 5, or multiples of 10, or quarters and halves of 100, as 20, 40, 60, etc., or 50, 100, 150, etc. Avoid scale units of 3, 6, 7, 8, or 9, as they are difficult to read.

Start the scale from zero on amount charts. *Do* letter in the numeral zero at the base line. Omitting the zero causes the viewer to glance up the scale and mentally subtract one unit amount from the one above it in order to find the value of each unit. The zero stresses the fact that the chart *does* start from a zero base line, and therefore it gives a true unit value to the amount scale.

Don't fail to check the scale numerals after lettering. Errors often occur in their progression. A chart recently appeared in a report with the upper units of the scale on the left reading 80, 100, *120*, while the right scale read 80, 100, *110*. It was particularly bad in this case, as the last plotting read 105 according to the right-hand scale, when the amount was actually 110.

THE HORIZONTAL GRID LABEL

When labeling the horizontal grid, which usually represents time or frequency, care must be taken to place the label directly under the plotted point. That is, the data plotted on the grid line should be labeled directly under that line, while plottings between the grids should be labeled under the space (see Fig. 2-7).

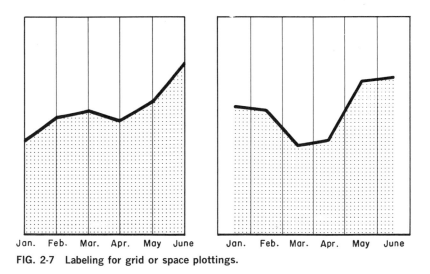

Jan.   Feb.   Mar.   Apr.   May   June   Jan.   Feb.   Mar.   Apr.   May   June

FIG. 2-7 Labeling for grid or space plottings.

If the divisions are for months, it is advisable to use the common abbreviations of the months rather than the first letter. Acceptable abbreviations are: Jan., Feb., Mar., Apr., May, June, July, Aug., Sept., Oct., Nov., and Dec.

When there is not room to label plottings monthly, label only the quarters. January, April, July, and October are generally used to designate quarters (see *a* in Fig. 2-8).

Quarterly data may be simply lettered 1, 2, 3, 4—representing the first, second, third, and fourth quarters—with the years under the numerals as in *b* in Fig. 2-8.

Annual data for a long period of time may be lettered every five or ten years or whatever intervals the space allows. However, keep the units of time equal throughout the layout even though the plottings may be irregular or incomplete (see *c* and *d* in Fig. 2-8).

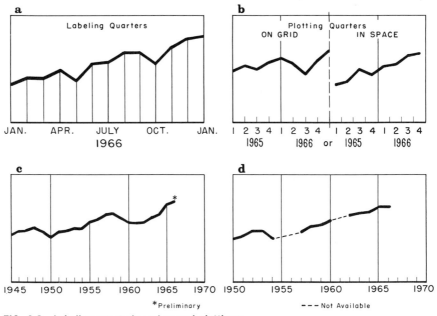

FIG. 2-8   Labeling quarterly and annual plottings.

SCALE CAPTIONS

Make captions for the vertical scale brief. They identify the numerals as cents, dollars, index, etc. The lettering should run horizontally and directly over the amount numerals. When captions are lettered vertically along the scale, either the chart or your head must be turned to read them. Making each element of the chart easy to read leads toward simplicity and a saving of time.

If space for the scale caption should be crowded, run a subcaption inside the grid under the top ruling (see Fig. 2-9).

It is not necessary to have a caption for the horizontal scale when only years are plotted. Other categories such as weeks, days, incomes, ages, must be clearly identified (see Fig. 4-25).

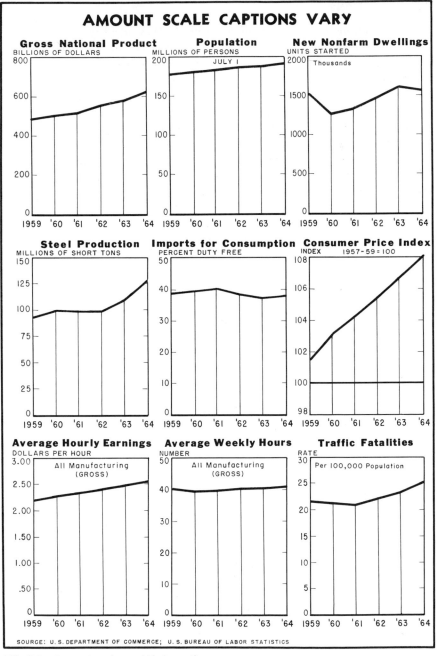

FIG. 2-9   Amount scales and their captions.

SCALE UNIT

Rechecking the scale units with the original data is of particular importance. Tables are not uniform in their format, and only too often the correct number of zeros is overlooked. This could result in the chart reading millions when billions is the right amount. For example, one source book of tables may carry, after the title, from two to eight or more lines of small type in which "thousands," "millions," "billions," or just "number" may appear referring to the data in the table. Other tables may carry a note or subtitle reading: "000,000 omitted"; "000 omitted"; "millions of"; "dollar amount in millions"; "amount of"; "in thousands"; "000s"; etc. Still others will carry the amount caption directly over the column of data. Because of these differences, one should read the fine print carefully.

Consider your subject matter, too. If the data do not seem to fit your own estimates of what they should be, question them. One of our best-known source books left off three zeros on one of its tables.

When dealing with large amounts, choose the simplest caption and scale for your chart (see Fig. 2-10).

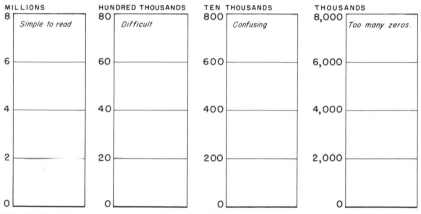

FIG. 2-10   Choosing amount scale and caption.

NOTES AND SOURCES

Notes and sources are lettered smaller than the rest of the chart, but must be clearly legible. Usually the source, indicating the origin of the data, appears at the bottom left corner of the chart. Notes should be reduced in wording to a minimum and appear in the bottom right corner. These may be in slightly larger lettering than the source and are more legible if lettered in uppercase and lowercase.

TEMPLATE LETTERING GUIDE

No matter what make of templates are used for lettering, a *lettering chart* will be found to be most advantageous for a quick visual reference concerning size, weight, and spacing of lettering needed for the job.

Figure 2-11 shows a few *actual* sizes of Leroy template lettering. Different weight pens were used with each size of template. Although template sizes run from No. 50 (0.05 in.) to No. 2000 (2 in.), only those sizes most commonly used need be laid out on the lettering-guide chart. Using uppercase and lowercase letters and numerals will meet all requirements.

Instead of the word "charting" lettered in Fig. 2-11, select a word commonly used in your industry or business, preferably one of about ten letters.

The lettering chart can be made on bristol board or sized cloth. The cloth, made of glutinous material, takes the ink readily and is easier to handle. It can be folded and laid directly on the work to determine the size and weight of lettering needed.

Always keep in mind legibility of lettering when reduction of a chart is involved.

TEMPLATE	LIGHT	Pen No.	AVERAGE	Pen	HEAVY	Pen
80	CHARTING 1965	000	CHARTING 1965	00	CHARTING 1965	0
100	CHARTING 1965 charting	000	CHARTING 1965 charting	00	CHARTING 1965 charting	0
120	CHARTING 1965 charting	00	CHARTING 1965 charting	0	CHARTING 1965 charting	1
140	CHARTING 1965 charting	0	CHARTING 1965 charting	1	CHARTIN 1965 charting	2
175	CHARTI 1965 charting	1	CHARTI 1965 charting	2	CHAR 1965 charting	3
200	CHART 1965 charting	1	CHART 1965 charting	2	CHAR 1965 charting	3
240 — and up to 2000	CHAR 1965 charting	2	CHA 1965 charting	3	CHA 1965 charting	4

FIG. 2-11   Variation in template lettering by use of pen number.

FOTOTYPE

Fototype was used for titling most charts and maps in this book. Figure 2-12 shows the pads of Fototype stored in a steel file and in a handy file folder. The letters are printed in blue on the working side and in black on the reverse side. Tear off the required letters and, with the blue side up, align them in the composing stick as shown. Press double-coated, pressure-sensitive Scotch tape across the letters. Remove from the composing stick and trim surplus edges. Turning over the strip of lettering and positioning it on the chart will result in black lettering for the finished title.

Other commercial lettering used was Deca-Dry and Cello-Tak, a dry-transfer process. The adhesive types were Formatt, Artype, Visitype, and Craft-Type.

FIG. 2-12   Fototype cabinet, Fototypettes file folder, composing stick, and font catalogue. (Fototype, Inc., Chicago, Ill.)

MISSPELLED WORDS

It is exasperating to find a misspelled word on the finished copy. It is not always from ignorance of spelling that this happens; it is more often caused by the concentration and concern of the letterer in his spacing and forming of individual letters. Then too, he often thinks ahead faster than he can letter, causing him to drop a letter. For these reasons, it is wise to check charts for spelling.

Fortunately the questionable lettering in Fig. 2-13 was caught before it reached the printer.

REVERSING CHARACTERS

With the variety of lettering methods and devices on the market, it is virtually impossible to make a character of the alphabet in reverse. But it does happen occasionally in hand lettering and in stenciling, through negligence or lack of knowledge of the correct form of the character. The most commonly reversed letters are E, N, and S (see Fig. 2-13).

Letters *have* been used in reverse to attract attention. A deputy police chief had a traffic warning painted on the street with the *e* in *Children* purposely reversed. He felt drivers seeing it would slow down. The same word is used by a toy store with the *n* and *r* reversed. Such incidents usually appear as an eye-catcher in advertisements. This practice, however, is not for charts or graphic displays. If used, it could possibly lead to distrust of your facts.

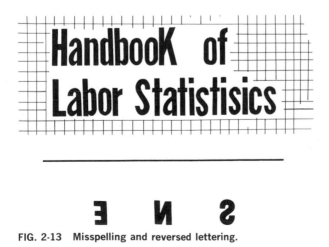

FIG. 2-13 Misspelling and reversed lettering.

WORDING FOR CHARTS

Wording for charts should be given to the draftsman either in written or in typed form. Verbal information is not always understood. For example, one chart appeared with the title "Drop in *Week* Prices" instead of "Drop in *Wheat* Prices."

WEIGHT OF LINES

The weight of line work on the standard statistical chart is as important as the size of lettering to attain a balanced look.

After the chart is laid out in pencil, it is a good idea to try out different line weights for curves, base line, border, and grids on a slip of bristol board. While weights of all lines differ with the size of the chart, all should be in proportion to that size. Think of a chart's use and draw lines suitable for it.

When deciding the comparative weights of lines for charts, diagrams, and maps, consider whether they are to be reduced in reproduction or used as originals. Figure 2-14 shows various widths of lines and their corresponding widths reduced. The following are comments on the heaviest to lightest weights of lines.

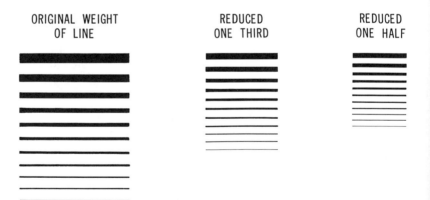

FIG. 2-14   Line reduction.

THE CURVE LINE

The curve or trend line should be the most prominent, as it carries the message. A smooth curve can afford to be heavier than one of active movement. Avoid drafting a steep slope to a sharp point, as it is then difficult to read the amount correctly (see Fig. 2-18).

Multiple curves on a chart can be lighter in weight than a single-trend curve; the width of lines depends upon the number of curves and their movement (see Fig. 2-15).

When symbol and solid-line curves are of the same importance, drafting the symbol-patterned lines slightly wider will give less attention to the solid trend line. For line patterns see Fig. 2-18.

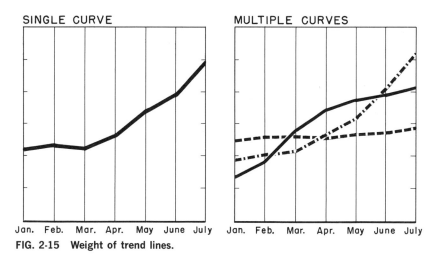

FIG. 2-15   Weight of trend lines.

THE BORDER

When a border is used to frame a chart, it should be lighter in weight than trend lines. A single line is best, as it will reproduce sharp and even. Double-line borders when reduced, if not properly drafted, have a tendency to run together or the lighter of the two lines may appear uneven or broken at intervals.

A chart without a border line has some advantage. It is not limited to a designated area. The irregular white space surrounding it makes it more adaptable to any page size. It may be more readily placed either horizontally or vertically on the page, as long as the reduction in the size of the chart does not destroy legibility of lettering (see Fig. 2-16).

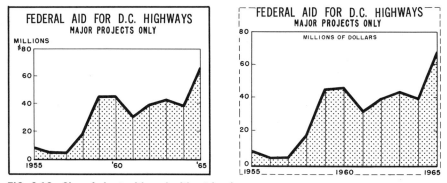

FIG. 2-16   Size of chart with and without border.

THE BASE LINE

The base line is the line of reference and should be the heaviest of the grid rulings. This is the zero line on the amount chart, the 100 line on the index chart, or any grid line used as a *base* for comparison.

The base line will generally be heavier on bar, column, and surface charts than on line charts, as those types have larger inked areas.

GRID LINES

The outside grid rulings are made slightly heavier than the lightweight rulings of the plotting grid. This is not because the framing grid is more important, but because it gives the chart a more finished look.

The number of grid lines is determined by the purpose of the chart, the degree of reading accuracy required, and the type and style of the chart. Only those scale rulings essential to guide the eye in reading and evaluating the plotted data need be drawn. Too many grid lines tend to obscure and add confusion to the purpose of the chart.

Chart 1b in Fig. 2-17 shows the grid stopping at the total curve "All Establishments." This helps to visually accent the fact that there is a total and two components. This is not stressed in chart 1a, where the grid is carried to the top of the chart.

In chart 2a, Fig. 2-17, the grid stopping at the highest curve makes the lower category appear of lesser importance. Chart 2b gives a clearer picture for comparing these amounts.

It is important, therefore, to know when the grid should be drawn to the *top* of the grid frame and when it should stop at the top trend, where the eye follows the silhouette of that curve.

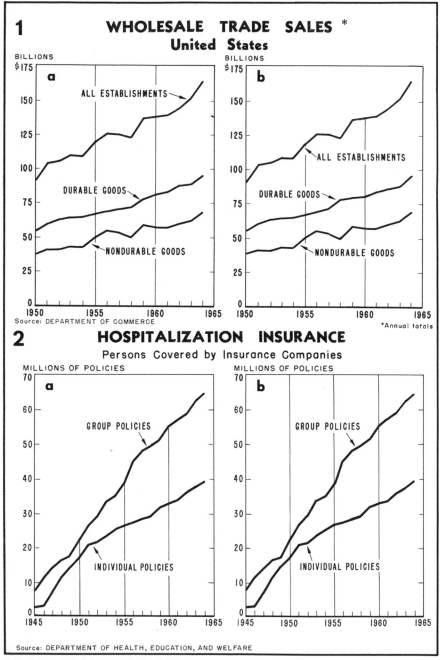

FIG. 2-17   When to complete grid lines.

TICKS

Ticks or stubs indicate the scale units when the grid lines are not fully drawn. They are light in weight and should not be too numerous or too long.

ARROWS

Arrows used to identify curves appear best if drawn at right angles to the slope of the curve to be labeled. Keep the style simple and distinct, not curved and overemphasized (see Fig. 2-17).

CONSTRUCTING WIDE TREND LINES

When the trend of a wide curve line is very active, there is always the danger of misreading the plotting if the steep slopes are drafted to a sharp point. Rounding this point by half the width of the curve will not only improve the appearance of the chart but show a more accurate amount reading (see Fig. 2-18).

To construct such a wide line, use a ruling pen and small compass or drop-bow pen, which is especially designed for drawing small circles.

Connect the plotted data to establish the trend. At each plotting draw a circle, the diameter of which will be the desired width of the curve (see Fig. 2-18). Following the trend, draw tangents to these circles but do not extend the ruling beyond the circle in such a manner that angles or sharp points are formed. The *rounded look* at each plotting not only carries the eye to the next plotting, but gives the most accurate reading for a wide curve.

These wide curves can be made with a variety of mechanical devices on the market, such as Leroy, Wrico, Speedball, Payzant, or any pen with a round point. They have a wide range of widths, and with practice can be easily handled (see Fig. 2-18).

TAPES FOR TRENDS

When using tapes for trend lines, the rounded effect can readily be obtained in the narrower widths. Ease the tape into position by holding a blunt bevel-edged instrument on the adhered tape at the plotting point. As the tape slants to the new position, it will ruffle or pleat slightly at the turn. Press these folds down firmly and continue to the next point. For wider tapes, the turn can be made smoother by snipping a V out of the tape with a pair of small, sharp scissors. Practice will show how much and where to cut for a designated slope (see Fig. 2-18).

PATTERNED TAPES

The choice of *patterns* used for trend lines depends upon the number of trends and closeness of plotting. See that some part of the pattern fits over the plotted point so as to give the most accurate reading (see line patterns in Fig. 2-18). Select contrasting, but straight dot-and-dash patterns (see tape patterns in Fig. 2-18).

If the trends do not cross too frequently, all solid lines will look neater than a series of patterns (see Figs. 2-17 and 4-17).

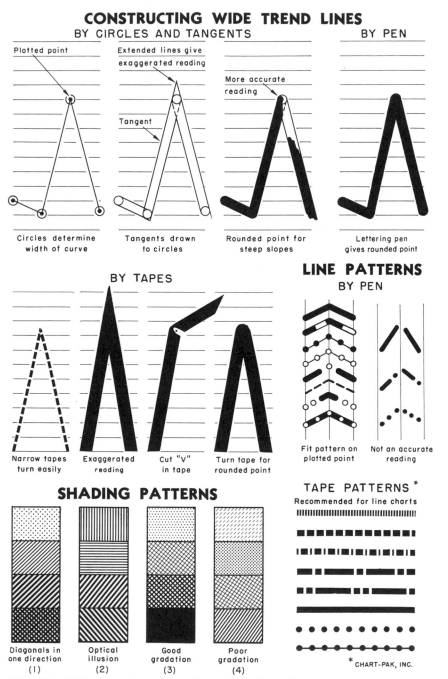

CONSTRUCTING WIDE TREND LINES
BY CIRCLES AND TANGENTS

Plotted point

Extended lines give exaggerated reading

More accurate reading

Tangent

Circles determine width of curve

Tangents drawn to circles

Rounded point for steep slopes

BY PEN

Lettering pen gives rounded point

BY TAPES

Narrow tapes turn easily

Exaggerated reading

Cut "V" in tape

Turn tape for rounded point

LINE PATTERNS
BY PEN

Fit pattern on plotted point

Not an accurate reading

SHADING PATTERNS

Diagonals in one direction
(1)

Optical illusion
(2)

Good gradation
(3)

Poor gradation
(4)

TAPE PATTERNS *
Recommended for line charts

* CHART-PAK, INC.

FIG. 2-18   Making heavy trend lines. Tape and shading patterns.

CROSSHATCHING AND SHADING FILMS

Crosshatching or shading should appear in any area on a chart or map that has a *value*, whether the data are of statistical, economical, or other status.

A pattern or shading should be applied to each component of a subdivided-column, -bar, or -surface chart. No numerical area should be left white. The only exception is when the background of a chart or the area around a map or chart is shaded. This will make the white area stand out relative to any crosshatched or colored areas (see Figs. 2-22 and 9-3).

Without a pattern, the resulting white area makes the bars and columns of a chart appear weak and distorted. Lack of pattern in the subdivided-surface chart divides the strata and gives the appearance of a shaded zone chart (see Figs. 2-19 and 5-13).

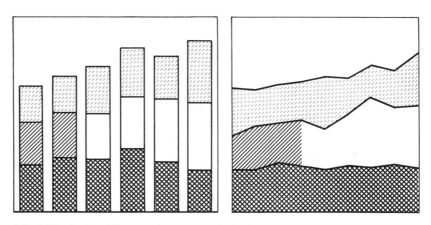

FIG. 2-19   Avoid white areas in component charts.

COMMERCIAL CROSSHATCH PATTERNS

Crosshatched films are available in a wide range of patterns suitable for various fields of art and drafting. Some are adhesive, pressure-sensitive, or rub-on; some have mat or gloss surfaces; and some are heat resistant. Which type to select depends upon the use of the chart or method of reproduction. Check chosen patterns with a reducing glass to see if there is enough contrast between them when reduced.

All patterns in this book are commercially printed shading films such as Contak, Craf-Tone, Formatt, Visitype, and Zip-A-Tone. For the black areas on charts and maps, a medium red Zip-A-Tone shading sheet was used. It is advisable to use red instead of black or heavily printed patterns, as the inked outline of the original easily shows through the transparent red overlay while working on the chart. Red appears black when reproduced for black-and-white copy.

HAND CROSSHATCHING

When commercial patterned materials are not available, fairly accurate crosshatching may be made by using a strip of cross-section paper and sliding a triangle along a T square, drawing a line at each printed division (see Fig. 2-20).

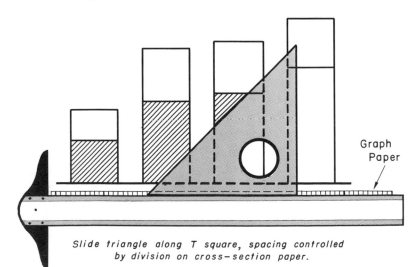

Graph
Paper

*Slide triangle along T square, spacing controlled
by division on cross-section paper.*

FIG. 2-20   Method of hand crosshatching.

COLOR AND TINT SHADING

The use of color and tints for shading has its advantages and disadvantages. It is quicker to perceive the same color in various tinted plottings and to identify it with the legend than to follow several black-and-white patterns. Colors, too, are more attractive when a harmonious effect is achieved. However, there is no visual progression of colors that can identify variations of amounts as clearly as can be shown with the many gradations of crosshatching. The nearest approach to this would be varying the value of the tint or shade of one color.

THE AIRBRUSH

The use of an airbrush to spray tints or shades of colors on the original presentation will give varying value effects. Experience with an airbrush will result in an even gradation of three or four values of a color.

SHADING SHEETS

Adhesive-backed shading sheets, waxed or pressure-sensitive, may be used directly on the pictorial. Bourges Cutocolor and Colotone have a good choice of values. A variety of line and dot patterns and some colors may be found in Artype, Contak, Craf-Tone, Formatt, and Zip-A-Tone sheets.

Figure 2-21 shows halftone screen tint blocks in varying percents of dots. Their value changes with the choice of screen used in reproduction.

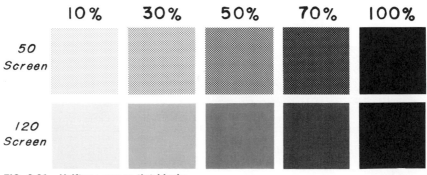

FIG. 2-21   Halftone screen tint blocks.

STYLIZING

Stylizing is giving a chart a certain *style*, that is, presenting it in a manner that attracts. One may stylize an annual report, exhibit, brochure, advertising article, or other visual need. But in attracting, the chart must not be distorted or overdecorated in such a way that the message in the chart is obscured.

Chart 1 in Fig. 2-22 would do for a company report. It is simple and it can readily be seen that earnings increased steadily while weekly hours dropped slightly. Usually a statistical table is in the report to give historical data. In this case, annual figures from 1945 to 1965 would give the reader actual amounts if he were interested.

When publishing tables representing data plotted in a chart, begin with the earliest date. It is confusing to refer to a table for data plotted from 1945 to 1965 and find that the statistics run from 1965 to 1945.

In chart 2, Fig. 2-22, the trend line is distorted by being drawn to a sharp point instead of being rounded at the plotted point. 1952 and 1959 should read 59.1 and 69.0, respectively (see Fig. 2-18).

Chart 3 in Fig. 2-22 with its three-dimensional effect is almost impossible to read correctly. The artist here, in attempting to be dramatic, merely lost his true message.

The stylized chart must be carefully planned concerning:

1. *Art work and layout*
2. *Balanced degree of shading*
3. *Design of lettering*

Overdecoration and freak layouts are misleading. The purpose of a chart is to display facts, not to disguise them.

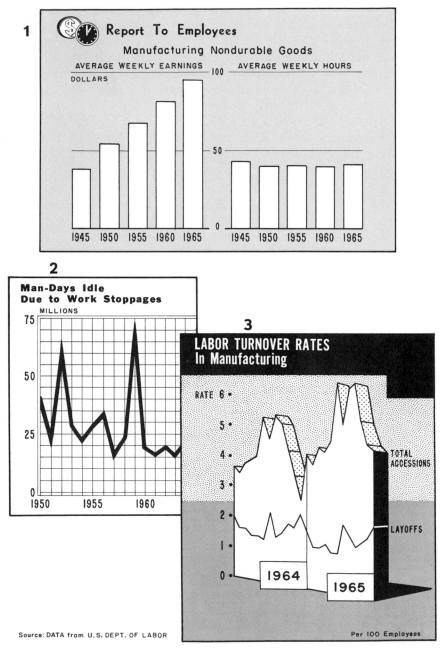

1

Report To Employees
Manufacturing Nondurable Goods

AVERAGE WEEKLY EARNINGS   AVERAGE WEEKLY HOURS
DOLLARS

100

50

0

1945 1950 1955 1960 1965   1945 1950 1955 1960 1965

2

**Man-Days Idle
Due to Work Stoppages**

MILLIONS

75

50

25

0

1950   1955   1960

3

LABOR TURNOVER RATES
In Manufacturing

RATE 6

5

4   TOTAL
      ACCESSIONS

3

2   LAYOFFS

1

0   1964   1965

Per 100 Employees

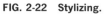

Source: DATA from U.S. DEPT. OF LABOR

FIG. 2-22   Stylizing.

THREE

Cheating by Charting

There are few of us who at one time or another have not exaggerated or shaded the truth by bragging or playing down a story. What we say may not be an untruth, but we want to stress one point in our story to a certain party and a different fact in it to another listener.

The same bragging or playing down can artfully appear in many types of charts. When and how do these distortions occur? They may be cleverly planned or may unwittingly happen during the production of the visual. The most commonly occurring distortions and illusions are exemplified here.

THE FLEXIBLE GRID

One of the easiest things to do to give more movement to the trend of a curve or to make it appear less active is to expand or to contract the horizontal or vertical axis of the chart. The charts in Fig. 3-1 show a correctly scaled trend and six ways the visual image changes by expanding or contracting the grid layout.

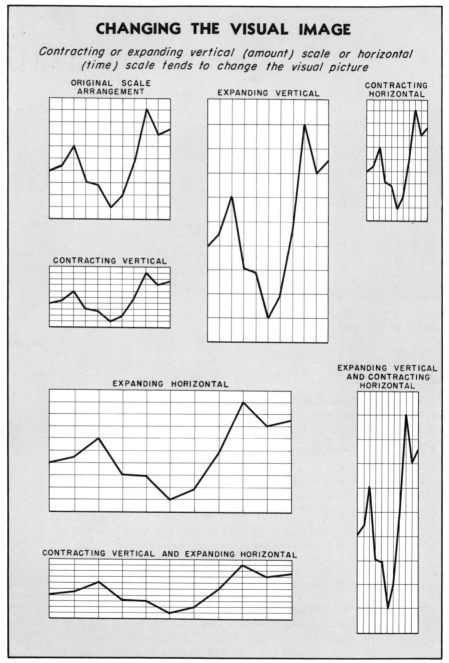

FIG. 3-1 Contracting and expanding the grid.

SKIPPING THE GRID

A familiar layout in reports and advertisements is seen in Fig.
3-2A. In order to dramatize the story, a little fudging is done with
the time scale. It is not noticeable at a casual glance that the time
sequence is not uniform. It seems to be a neat, clean-cut, see-how-
we've-grown story. Even the dates lettered at right angles to the
base line make the irregular date plotting less noticeable.

Chart *B* in Fig. 3-2 shows what the trend looks like when laid
out with the correct grid spacing for each year. Amount plottings
for the given years are the same. Spread out this way is not as
dramatic, but is the true story.

Chart *G* in Fig. 3-12 makes no allowance for the missing years.

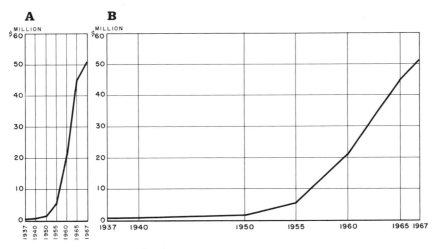

FIG. 3-2   Spacing an irregular time sequence.

THE BROKEN AMOUNT SCALE

The broken amount scale is commonly used to enlarge on a story. Watch out for it, as it is bound to exaggerate; differences appear greater, and trends seem steeper.

It is essential that charts with an arithmetic scale begin at the zero base line in order to show the true variation in movements. Compare the visual differences between charts *A* and *B* in Fig. 3-3.

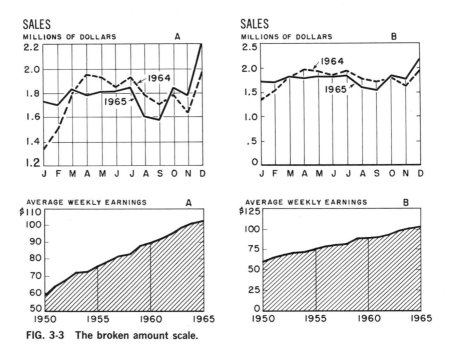

FIG. 3-3   The broken amount scale.

An even greater distortion of the true relationship of amounts occurs when columns or component surface layouts break their scales (see Fig. 3-4).

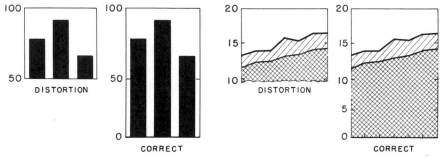

FIG. 3-4   Distortions when breaking the grid.

The draftsman may have indicated that the grid was broken by using several methods, but that is risky. The distorted impression is the one remembered, not the broken scale (see Fig. 3-5).

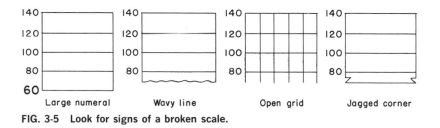

FIG. 3-5   Look for signs of a broken scale.

ILLUSIONS IN CHARTING

Optical illusions can occur, intentionally or unintentionally, when drafting charts.

Many a trend line needs sufficient grid for one to properly read the plotting. In Fig. 3-6, the plottings on lines A and B for years 1955 and 1960 are identical. However, because of the slope of the trends in the chart without the grid, the plotted points for 1955 on A and B appear closer together than the same plottings for 1960. The drawn grid helps correct this illusion.

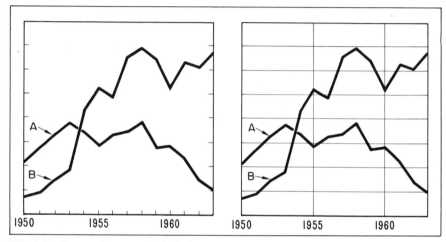

FIG. 3-6   Overcoming an optical illusion.

SHADING ILLUSIONS

Many illusions are caused on charts by crosshatching. A series of columns with diagonals slanted in opposite directions will cause the spacing between the columns to appear uneven and the amounts plotted distorted, and the column outlines will not seem parallel (see part 1, Fig. 3-7).

Horizontal rulings tend to visually reduce the plottings, while vertical lines enlarge them. The columns in part 2, Fig. 3-7 seem to be tied in the middle like a sheaf of grain.

All patterned shadings should be of distinctive tonal value to be of good contrast. Chart *H* in Fig. 3-12 has poor tonal value and opposing patterns. Diagonals should have the same directional angle (see shading patterns in Fig. 2-18). Alternating dark and light shadings is not recommended, as optical illusion can again occur. The dark patterns can make the light patterns appear of less value.

When shading a simple surface chart, emphasize the trend by shading from the zero line to the curve. Figure 5-4 shows how shading can visually affect the trend.

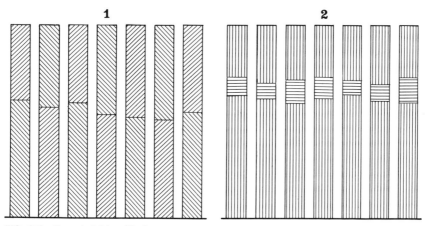

FIG. 3-7   Crosshatching illusions.

THE ILLUSIVE THREE-DIMENSIONAL CHART

In the mid-1940s and 1950s the three-dimensional chart was popular. Fortunately that vogue seems to be passing. While some were interesting and attractive, they were for the most part practically impossible to read or interpret directly. Comparisons were difficult to make, and scales had to be visually adjusted so that amounts could be read. Such a process required mental and optic gymnastics (see chart 3 in Fig. 2-22).

True relationships in the three-dimensional chart could easily be hidden by artistic perspectives and shadings used (see Fig. 3-12*F*).

THE MISLEADING PICTOGRAPH

There are many pitfalls to watch out for in the use of pictographs. The charts in Fig. 10-5 show the wrong and right layouts of pictorials when comparing units of measure. No matter what their width, units should be centered over each other for a correct comparison.

It is an easy matter to give false impressions of a comparison by designing symbols wider or narrower than need be and spacing them without regard to the unit of measure. One row of symbols then appears longer than the other, when in reality the number may be smaller.

Pictographs representing a man, animal, basket of food, or other objects that we normally think of as having three dimensions or volume are often pictured as two-dimensional drawings. Here, if the data are not given, it is difficult to judge whether the drawing has been calculated by cube root or square root.

Comparing sizes of pictographs can be most deceiving. The common error is to draw one man twice the size of another when the data state that there are twice the number of men in company A as in company B. Don't let your first glance satisfy you. Figure 10-12*B* depicts a correct third-dimensional drawing for comparing numbers of hogs.

THE TRICKY INDEX

The index chart can prove invaluable when properly used. However, indiscriminately used, it can play havoc with a trend when one compares it visually with the base line. The 100 percent line represents the base on an index chart. The data are calculated on a selected base year (see the discussion of index charts in Sec. 4). If the lowest value in a series is chosen as the base year, the indexes will be *above* the accented base line, whereas choosing the highest value will bring the series *below* the 100 line.

Figure 3-8 plots the data in amounts in three selected base years. Because 1954 had the lowest value in the series, the trend appears above the base line; 1964, having the highest value, causes the trend to appear below the base.

Note whether you are viewing amounts or indexes. Many times the 100 line is not accented to give this first clue.

Learn to see details. There is quite a difference between simply looking at a chart and seeing it. Looking is your first visual impression, while seeing involves the studying of distinct parts of the visual.

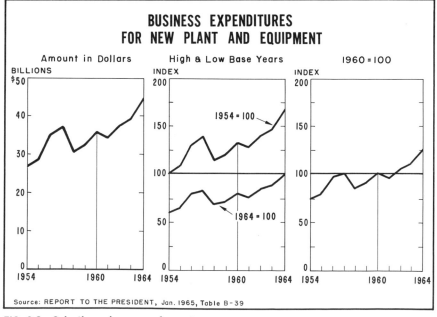

FIG. 3-8   Selecting a base year for a story.

THE MULTISCALE COMPLEX

You will come across numerous charts using two or more scales purporting to prove a point. Beware of them. It is too easy to adjust the scales to make one trend visually appear greater in amount and more important than another trend.

Figure 3-9 shows that by changing the population scale in the chart in Fig. 4-12 the "Personal Income" trend assumes more importance.

Check to see that all scales begin from zero and that there is a scale unit relationship (see the discussion of multiple scales in Sec. 4).

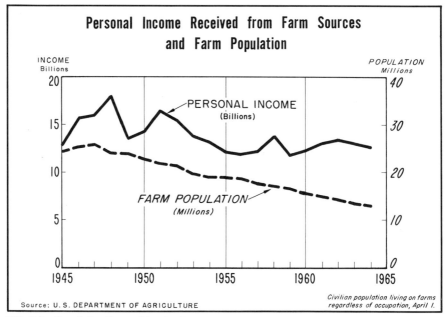

FIG. 3-9   Scrutinize the multiscale chart.

ILLUSIONS ON MAPS

A popular representation of data used by feature writers in magazines and newspapers is the shaded map. Which states are selected makes a drastic difference in how impressive the visual report is.

The three shaded maps in Fig. 3-10 compare the growth of United States federal expenses with the personal income received from all sources by the residents of those states. Such data are not concerned with actual land areas, except to express a dramatic picture; hence the use of the Western and Midwestern states.

A less striking effect is shown when the Eastern states are shaded, as in Fig. 3-11, because incomes are higher in the Middle-Atlantic states and the areas of the Eastern states are much smaller than the Western.

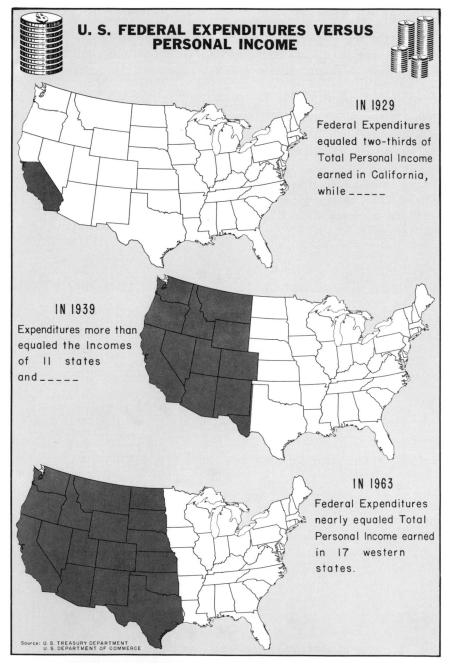

U. S. FEDERAL EXPENDITURES VERSUS PERSONAL INCOME

IN 1929
Federal Expenditures equaled two-thirds of Total Personal Income earned in California, while _ _ _ _ _

IN 1939
Expenditures more than equaled the Incomes of 11 states and _ _ _ _ _

IN 1963
Federal Expenditures nearly equaled Total Personal Income earned in 17 western states.

Source: U. S. TREASURY DEPARTMENT
U. S. DEPARTMENT OF COMMERCE

FIG. 3-10   The story grows dramatic when Western states are shaded.

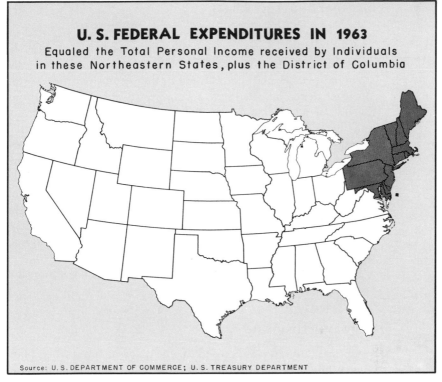

U. S. FEDERAL EXPENDITURES IN 1963

Equaled the Total Personal Income received by Individuals
in these Northeastern States, plus the District of Columbia

Source: U. S. DEPARTMENT OF COMMERCE; U. S. TREASURY DEPARTMENT

FIG. 3-11   Shading Eastern states minimizes the story.

INTERPRETING THE VISUAL

This knowledge of whether the factual story is being told or whether the data have been *graphically* distorted is essential in chart interpretation. The very fact that the presentation is visual makes it stronger and more lasting in the memory of the viewer. Whether the trend of a curve soars upward, stays level, or drops sharply, or whether the bars show a greater or lesser difference remains with a viewer much longer than the relative statistics do.

Statistics can be as misleading as the intentionally distorted chart is. Surveys and samples can be biased, correlations too small, factors missing, improper measures taken—not to mention the possible prejudice of the writer or speaker. But fortunately, as the art of graphic presentation advances, more listeners and viewers are becoming aware of these pitfalls and give heed to them; and more designers of charts are being artistic without confounding the true story.

Remember: Visual presentations have a more lasting impression than the data they represent.

DISPLAY ILLUSIONS

Optical illusions *can* be used to advantage at times when planning exhibits, mounting pictures, and laying out brochures and similar public relations pieces.

In Fig. 3-12A, the column appears longer than the base line. This is because we have a tendency to see vertical lines longer than horizontal lines. In diagram B, the figures are all the same size, but the background, drawn in perspective, gives the illusion that the figure to the right is larger. In C, the two white squares are identical in size, but the wider border makes the upper white square appear smaller. In D, the relationship of the lines to the circles makes the one closest to the lines appear larger than the circle in space. In E, the left part of the straight line is just as long as the right part; the directional arrows make them appear uneven. It is what the eye takes in when looking at these figures that causes us to see these illusions. The squares, the circles, the lines—all have a relationship to some background. We do not see them as some distant visual unit, but as a whole unit. Check your display and see if you can use such illusions to advantage.

Watch Out For These!

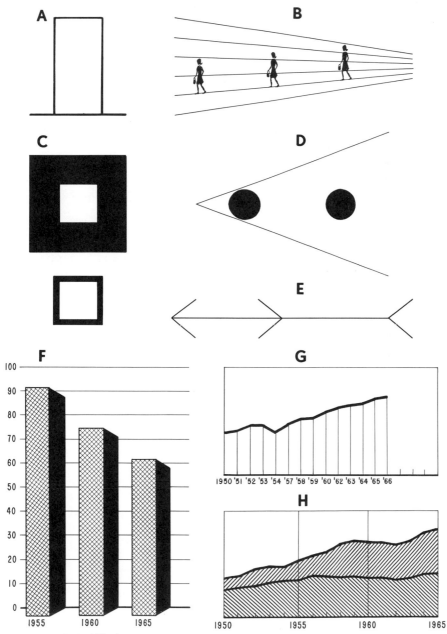

FIG. 3-12   Optical illusions.

FOUR

Line Charts

A statistical chart can be many things. To some it is the analysis of their data. To others it is a picture that means more to them than a column of numerals. To still others it may be a confusion of lines and bars. It is because of these differences, that the right type of chart must be chosen and presented simply and clearly in graphic form to put across its specific message.

TYPES OF CHARTS

There have been many surveys and tests concerning which type of chart is easiest to *read*. Some have concluded that the pie or sector chart is the best (see Fig. 8-1). Other surveys showed that bar and column charts were more popular (see Fig. 1-1). But these were not tests of good *graphic presentation*. The pie chart may be cluttered with too many sectors and become difficult to letter and read. Bar and column charts may be poorly spaced or shaded with patterns that cause optical illusions.

The real test is choosing the *type* of chart that stresses its objective and then rendering it in a well-balanced visual presentation. The first step toward this is to know the *correct names* and *specific uses* of the different types of charts.

USING THE QUADRANTS

Figure 4-1 shows the four *quadrants* formed by the intersection of the horizontal line (axis X, the abscissa) and the vertical line (axis Y, the ordinate). The point where the two axes intersect is zero or the point of origin. From this point plus values are measured upward and to the right; minus values downward and to the left (see 1 in Fig. 4-1).

Quadrant I is the most commonly used for time series and frequency distribution. In such charts the horizontal axis shows the time units or size of intervals, while the vertical axis measures the amount. Chart 2 in Fig. 4-1 shows the plotting of a simple trend chart in quadrant I. Most charts for popular presentation are made in this quadrant, as it is positive in respect to both axes.

Values plotted in quadrants I and IV are positive *and* negative in respect to the vertical Y scale. This is shown by the deviation column chart plotted in chart 3, Fig. 4-1. This could also have been a line chart (see Fig. 5-18). Chart 4 in Fig. 4-1 shows a deviation bar chart plotted in quadrants I and II.

Quadrant III is not ordinarily used, as both the X and Y values are negative.

THE LINE CHART

The line or curve chart is the most widely used method of presenting statistics graphically. It is simple to construct. The plotted points of the data are connected by a solid or symbol line. The fluctuation of this line shows the variations in the trend (see chart 2, Fig. 4-1).

THE QUADRANTS
FORMED BY INTERSECTION OF AXES X AND Y

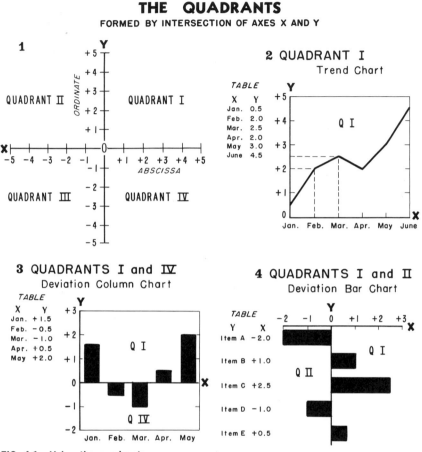

1

2 QUADRANT I
Trend Chart

TABLE	
X	Y
Jan.	0.5
Feb.	2.0
Mar.	2.5
Apr.	2.0
May	3.0
June	4.5

3 QUADRANTS I and IV
Deviation Column Chart

TABLE	
X	Y
Jan.	+1.5
Feb.	−0.5
Mar.	−1.0
Apr.	+0.5
May	+2.0

4 QUADRANTS I and II
Deviation Bar Chart

TABLE	
Y	X
Item A	−2.0
Item B	+1.0
Item C	+2.5
Item D	−1.0
Item E	+0.5

FIG. 4-1 Using the quadrants.

WHEN TO USE LINE CHARTS

The more popular uses of line charts are shown by the types of charts in Fig. 4-2:

1. *When data cover a long period of time (A)*

2. *When several series are compared on the same chart (B)*

3. *When the emphasis is on the movement rather than on the actual amount (C)*

4. *When trends of frequency distribution are presented (D)*

5. *When a multiple-amount scale is used (E)*

6. *When estimates, forecasts, interpolation, or extrapolation are to be shown (F)*

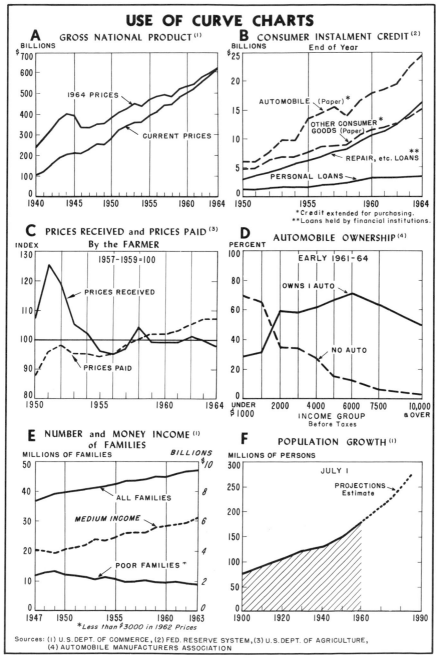

USE OF CURVE CHARTS

A GROSS NATIONAL PRODUCT[1]

B CONSUMER INSTALMENT CREDIT[2]
End of Year

*Credit extended for purchasing.
**Loans held by financial institutions.

C PRICES RECEIVED and PRICES PAID[3]
By the FARMER

D AUTOMOBILE OWNERSHIP[4]

E NUMBER and MONEY INCOME[1]
of FAMILIES

F POPULATION GROWTH[1]

Sources: (1) U.S. DEPT. OF COMMERCE, (2) FED. RESERVE SYSTEM, (3) U.S. DEPT. OF AGRICULTURE,
(4) AUTOMOBILE MANUFACTURERS ASSOCIATION

FIG. 4-2 When to use the line chart.

PLOTTING POINT DATA AND PERIOD DATA

The problem frequently arises as to whether the data for a time series are plotted in the space or on the grid line of the horizontal scale. This is because there are two kinds of time data, point data and period data.

Point data refer to a specific point or instant of time, such as assets at the beginning of the year, sales at the middle of the year, or employment at the end of the year. When point data are plotted as in Fig. 4-3, the *dates* are centered in the space of the horizontal scale. However, the point of time should be clearly noted on the chart. Monthly data should be treated similarly.

Period data refer to an entire period, such as total sales for each month or for each year, and weekly and monthly averages. The period data are plotted in the space with the *dates* centered under the plotted points (see Fig. 4-3).

POINT DATA   PERIOD DATA

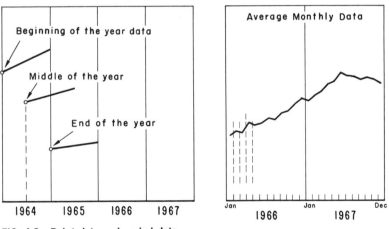

FIG. 4-3   Point data and period data.

Theoretically the vertical rulings designate the *points* of time, and the spaces between the rulings represent the *periods* of time. But both *point data* and *period data* are generally plotted on the vertical rulings for popular presentations. The nature of some data is more easily read when plotted on the grid, as the eye normally follows the rulings and reads the point where the curve crosses the grid.

The main thing to remember is to label whichever plotting point is used directly under the rulings or spaces (see Fig. 4-4).

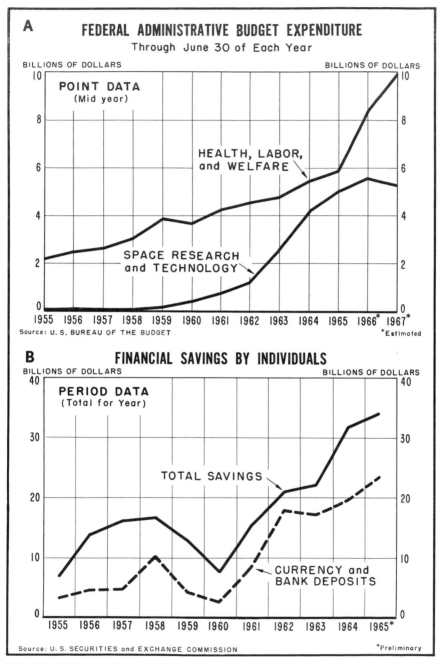

A FEDERAL ADMINISTRATIVE BUDGET EXPENDITURE
Through June 30 of Each Year

BILLIONS OF DOLLARS · BILLIONS OF DOLLARS

POINT DATA
(Mid year)

HEALTH, LABOR,
and WELFARE

SPACE RESEARCH
and TECHNOLOGY

1955 1956 1957 1958 1959 1960 1961 1962 1963 1964 1965 1966* 1967*
Source: U. S. BUREAU OF THE BUDGET   *Estimated

B FINANCIAL SAVINGS BY INDIVIDUALS

BILLIONS OF DOLLARS · BILLIONS OF DOLLARS

PERIOD DATA
(Total for Year)

TOTAL SAVINGS

CURRENCY and
BANK DEPOSITS

1955 1956 1957 1958 1959 1960 1961 1962 1963 1964 1965*
Source: U. S. SECURITIES and EXCHANGE COMMISSION   *Preliminary

FIG. 4-4   Plotting on the grid and in the space.

The following charts are more clearly read when plotted on the vertical rulings:

1. *When curves are plotted at varying intervals.* The chart in Fig. 4-5 shows the index of gross average weekly earnings plotted both quarterly and monthly.

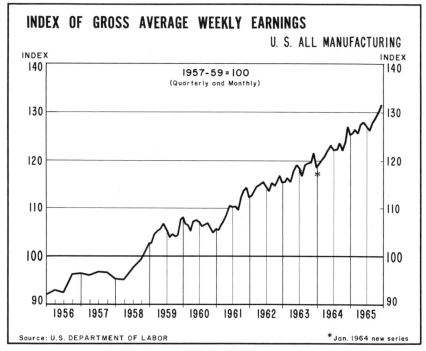

FIG. 4-5   Plotting trends for irregular intervals.

2. When data cover a long span of time. The yearly averages of the union membership curve, because of the length of time covered, identifies the five-year rulings more readily on the vertical grid than if it were plotted in the space. The break in the curve at 1955 occurred when the American Federation of Labor and the Congress of Industrial Organizations became a joint membership (see Fig. 4-6).

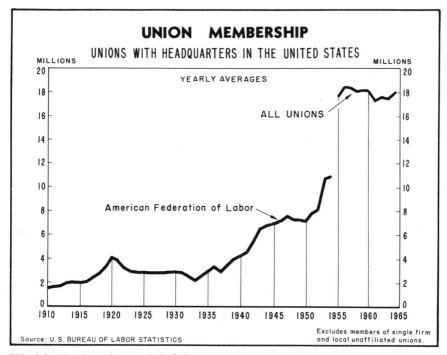

FIG. 4-6   Plotting a long period of time.

3. *When data are cumulative.* In Fig. 4-7, the cumulative data are easier to read when plotted on the vertical rulings. Note that Table 4-1 has a special cumulative column of data *for plotting only.*

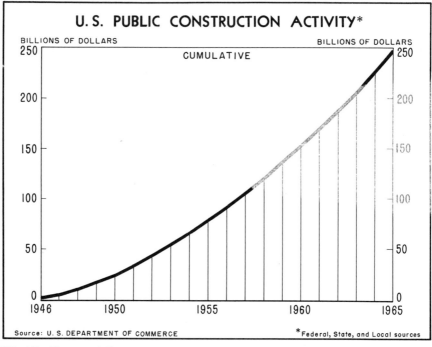

FIG. 4-7   The cumulative curve.

TABLE 4-1   *New Public Construction Activity, United States, 1946–1965 (Millions of Dollars)*

Year	Total	Cumulated for plotting	Year	Total	Cumulated for plotting
1946	2,231	2,231	1956	12,732	90,824
1947	3,319	5,550	1957	14,059	104,883
1948	4,704	10,254	1958	15,457	120,340
1949	6,269	16,523	1959	16,070	136,410
1950	6,866	23,389	1960	15,863	152,273
1951	9,255	32,644	1961	17,148	169,421
1952	10,779	43,423	1962	17,869	187,290
1953	11,242	54,665	1963	18,896	206,186
1954	11,712	66,377	1964	19,926	226,112
1955	11,715	78,092	1965	20,234	246,346

SOURCE: U.S. Department of Commerce, Bureau of the Census.

4. *When a step or staircase chart is plotted.* This type is more graphic when drawn on the vertical grid (see Fig. 4-8). Other forms of step diagrams are shown in this chapter.

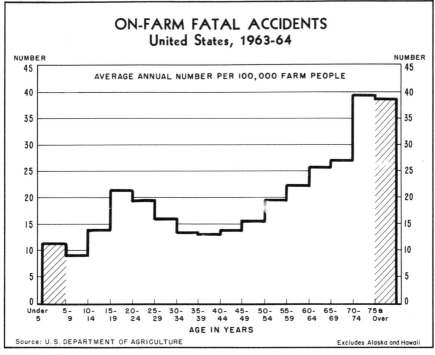

FIG. 4-8   The step or staircase chart.

ILLUSTRATIONS

Illustrations on a chart must be meaningful. Too often an illustration is used only for decoration. In Fig. 4-9, the little man, climbing upward, slipping, sitting on top of the peak, and then falling, is expressive of the nature of the trend.

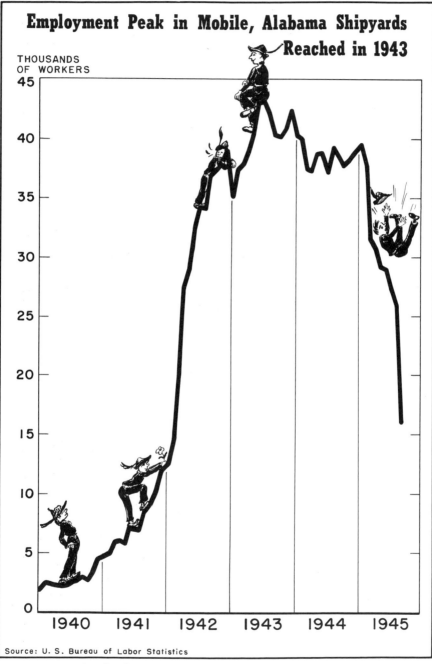

Employment Peak in Mobile, Alabama Shipyards Reached in 1943

THOUSANDS
OF WORKERS

Source: U. S. Bureau of Labor Statistics

FIG. 4-9   Illustrating the chart.

MULTIPLE-CURVE CHARTS

Multiple-curve charts compare two or more trends. If several trends appear concentrated in a section of the chart, it is better to plot the data on two or more charts. However, the *same unit-scale* measurement must be kept in order to hold the correct visual comparison.

In Fig. 4-10, it can readily be seen that six trends would be confusing if plotted in the 0-to-5 unit of the scale. Therefore the two smaller charts were made with the same unit scale to accommodate four of the trends.

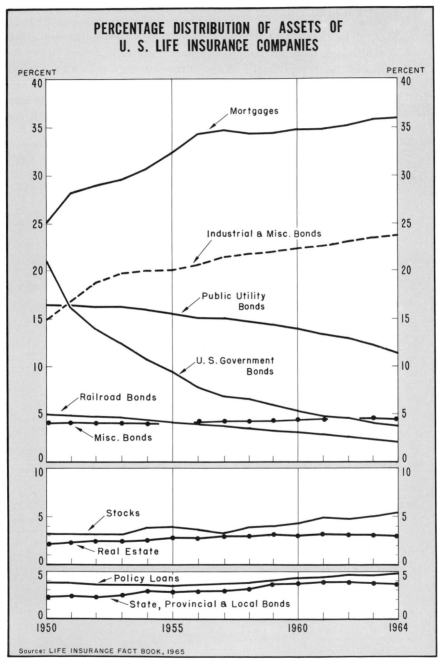

FIG. 4-10   Multiple-curve chart.

GROUPING CHARTS

The charts in part 1, Fig. 4-11, appear as a well-balanced group although they have *different* amount scales. It is easy to see the effect of World War II by the steady rise in the increase of campaigns and the amount of money raised.

Part 2 of Fig. 4-11 groups the trends of Consumer Price Indexes using the *same* unit amount scale throughout. This avoids any distortion when the trends are compared.

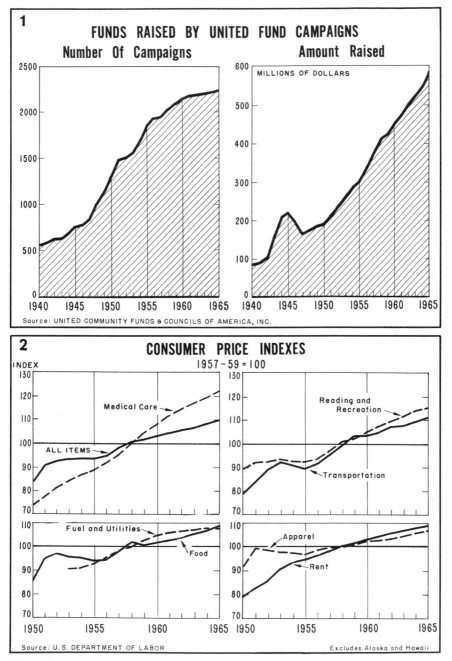

1

FUNDS RAISED BY UNITED FUND CAMPAIGNS

Number Of Campaigns   **Amount Raised**

MILLIONS OF DOLLARS

Source: UNITED COMMUNITY FUNDS & COUNCILS OF AMERICA, INC.

2

CONSUMER PRICE INDEXES

INDEX   1957-59 = 100

Medical Care

ALL ITEMS

Reading and Recreation

Transportation

Fuel and Utilities

Food

Apparel

Rent

Source: U.S. DEPARTMENT OF LABOR   Excludes Alaska and Hawaii

FIG. 4-11   Grouping related charts.

MULTIPLE-AMOUNT-SCALE CHARTS

Charts with multiple-amount scales, that is, those using two or more scales for comparing series of unlike units, are not suitable for popular presentation. The resulting chart is apt to be misleading, and it will be misinterpreted if the reader is not familiar with this type of graph.

If, however, multiple-amount scales are used, they should start from a common base line or zero. Care should be taken to identify the curve with its corresponding unit-amount scale. Both curve label and scale caption should carry this unit identification, that is, number, millions, etc. (see Fig. 4-12). In this chart, the *vertical* lettering of the scale and trend label refer to "Population," while all the *slant* lettering identifies "Personal Income."

In selecting the different amount scales, one should be certain that the unit divisions of each scale are directly opposite each other; that is, if the left scale is to include the plotted amount of 3.5 millions and the right scale is to include 69 millions, the left scale should go up by 1 million to 4, whereas each scale unit on the right should go by 20 millions to 80. Such a process divides the vertical amount grid of each scale into four equal units (see Fig. 4-13). Both scales should start from zero.

It is much easier to identify the components of a multiple-amount-scale chart if it is made in color. The charts in Fig. 4-13 show three methods of rendering the chart in black and white or color.

Farm Population and Income Received
from Farm Sources

POPULATION
Millions

INCOME
Billions

FARM POPULATION*
(Millions)

PERSONAL INCOME
(Billions)

*Civilian population living on farms,
regardless of occupation, April 1

Source: U. S. DEPARTMENT OF AGRICULTURE

FIG. 4-12   Multiple-amount scales.

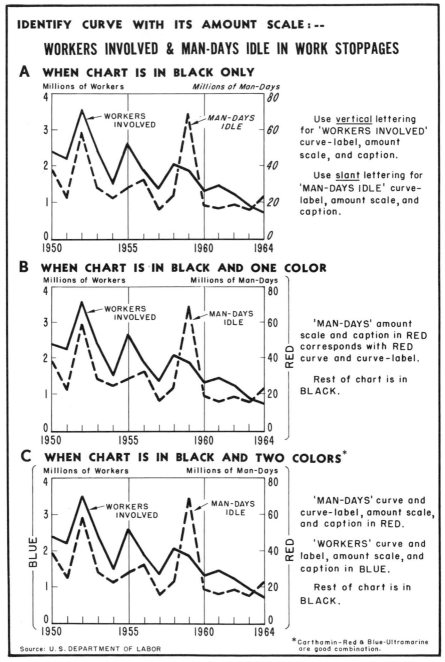

FIG. 4-13   Labeling black and white or color multiple-amount charts.

MULTIPLE-TIME CHARTS

Multiple-time charts provide a means of comparing monthly or
seasonal data of a *single* item for any number of selected years.
The chart in Fig. 4-14 compares egg prices in retail stores located
in urban areas. See Fig. 4-22 for comparing *periods* of time.

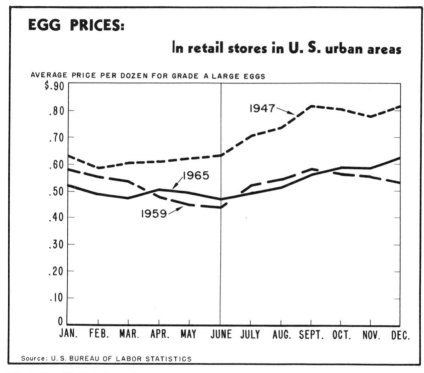

FIG. 4-14   Multiple-time chart.

THE INDEX CHART

The index chart is not the most popular chart for general presentation, but once understood it becomes invaluable. True, it can be misused purposely (see Sec. 3), but used meaningfully it can show the relation of a trend to a base year or period of time.

To change amounts into index numbers for plotting a trend, divide each given amount by the value of the *selected* base year and multiply the quotient by 100.

In Table 4-2, the year 1959 was *chosen* as the base year. The amount for that year, $400 billion, was divided into the amount for each year. Multiplying the results by 100 gives the index series on a 1959 base.

TABLE 4-2   *Total National Income, United States, 1955–1965*

Year	Billions of dollars	Index 1959 = 100
1955	331.0	82.8
1956	350.8	87.7
1957	366.1	91.5
1958	367.8	92.0
1959	400.0	100.0
1960	414.5	103.9
1961	427.3	106.8
1962	457.7	114.4
1963	481.1	120.3
1964	514.4	128.6
1965°	554.6	138.7

° Preliminary estimate.

Note: National income is the total net income earned in production.

SOURCE: U.S. Department of Commerce, Office of Business Economics.

Figure 4-15 shows the total national income in actual dollars and the index when based on the year 1959.

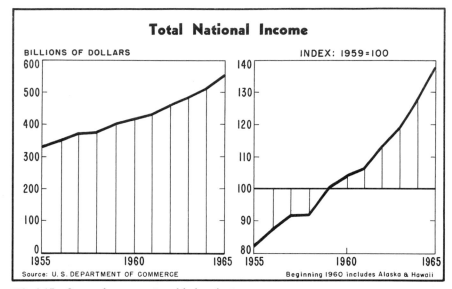

FIG. 4-15   Comparing amount and index charts.

CHANGING THE INDEX BASE

Most price and cost-of-living data are reported as indexes. These index numbers may be changed from one base to another by dividing the *known* index series by a *selected* base year or years. Multiply the quotient by 100 for the new series.

In the charts in Fig. 4-16, 1957–1959 = 100 was the known base (see Table 4-3). To change this base to 1935–1939 = 100, the given indexes for those five years were averaged (48.7) and divided into each index of the 1957–1959 series. The result multiplied by 100 gave the 1935–1939 = 100 data for plotting.

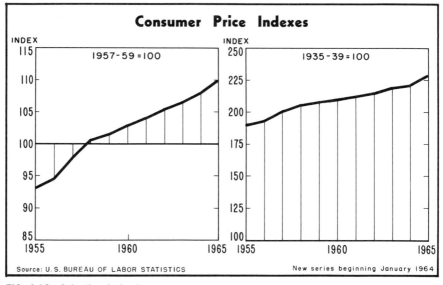

FIG. 4-16 Selecting index base.

TABLE 4-3   *Consumer Price Indexes for City Wage Earners and Clerical Workers (All Items 1957–1959 = 100)*

Year	Index	Year	Index	Year	Index	Year	Index
1935	47.8	1945	62.7	1955	93.3	1965	109.9
1936	48.3	1946	68.0	1956	94.7		
1937	50.0	1947	77.8	1957	98.0		
1938	49.1	1948	83.8	1958	100.7		
1939	48.4	1949	83.0	1959	101.5		
1940	48.8	1950	83.8	1960	103.1		
1941	51.3	1951	90.5	1961	104.2		
1942	56.8	1952	92.5	1962	105.4		
1943	60.3	1953	93.2	1963	106.7		
1944	61.3	1954	93.6	1964	108.1°		

° New series beginning January, 1964. See Department of Labor release, *Major Changes in The Consumer Price Index, March 3, 1964.*

Note: Data in italics are years used for 1935–1939 index base (see Fig. 4-16).

SOURCE: U.S. Department of Labor, Bureau of Labor Statistics.

Figure 4-17 compares the Consumer Price Index for three selected base periods. The chart begins at zero but maintains the heavy 100-base grid.

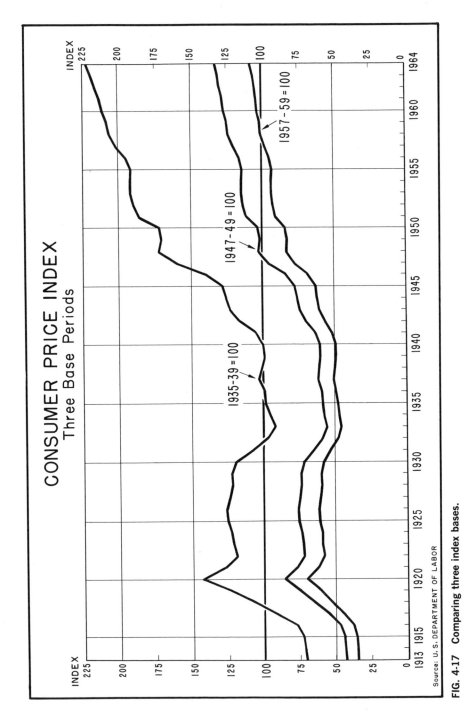

FIG. 4-17 Comparing three index bases.

WHEN TO USE INDEXES

Index charts are used to advantage:

1. *For comparing the relationship of two series which differ greatly in amount.* The first chart in Fig. 4-18 shows the difference in the magnitude of the actual amounts in financing hospital construction, while the index chart gives a relative picture of direct federal aid to the total funds (see Table 4-4).

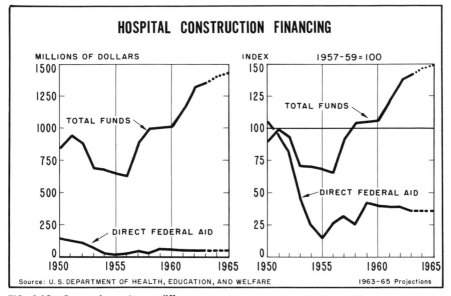

FIG. 4-18   Comparing extreme differences.

TABLE 4-4   *Hospital Construction Financing, United States, 1950–1965*

	Millions of dollars		Index 1957–1959 = 100	
Year	Total funds	Direct federal aid	Total funds	Direct federal aid
1950	843	146	88.2	105.8
1951	946	132	99.0	95.8
1952	889	113	93.0	81.9
1953	686	66	71.8	47.8
1954	670	35	70.1	25.4
1955	651	22	68.1	15.9
1956	628	37	65.7	26.8
1957	*879*	*45*	91.9	32.6
1958	*990*	*35*	103.6	25.4
1959	*998*	*58*	103.9	42.0
1960	1,005	56	105.1	40.5
1961	1,157	55	121.0	39.8
1962	1,322	55	138.3	39.8
1963°	1,360	50	142.3	36.2
1964°	1,415	50	148.0	36.2
1965°	1,440	50	150.6	36.2

° 1963–1965 projections.

Note: Data in italics are years used for index base.

SOURCE: U.S. Department of Health, Education, and Welfare. *Hospital Construction: Financing 1920–1965,* p. 35.

2. *When the relationship of two or more series of unlike basic units is to be shown.* Chart *A* in Fig. 4-19 shows the total number of unemployed persons and total benefits paid to them by using multiple-amount scales. Chart *B*, where the amounts have been converted to indexes, shows the relative difference in the trends more clearly. The index scale is easier to interpret than the multiple-amount scale in terms of relationship. But the base year must be selected cautiously.

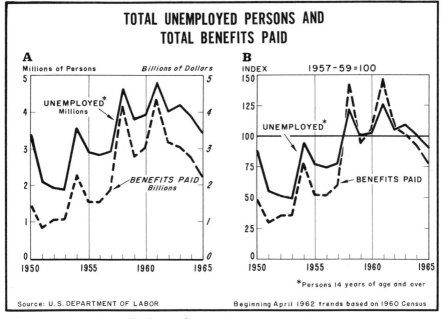

FIG. 4-19   Comparing unlike base units.

SELECTION OF BASE YEAR

This caution in selecting a base year for the index trend is essential. To choose a year when the data are low will cause the trend to be plotted above the 100 percent base line, and, in reverse, a high year will bring the trend below the base line.

As a rule, in historical series, a base year is selected during a time which is considered *normal*. Different phenomena and economic events influence this *normal-base* selection. A totally different visual story may be presented by the same data because of a difference of opinion concerning what year or period is considered a normal base.

But whichever year is selected, it is wise to have a sound reason for choosing it in order to back up your visual story.

For example, a corporation wanted to show that existing earnings were fair and sufficient when compared with the cost of living. They selected 1940 as a valid year on which to base this conclusion. On the other hand, the employees felt that 1957 to 1959 was a fair base and that although earnings appeared higher after this period, their earnings had been so much lower over a long period of time, that they should receive compensation for this loss. A 1965 base, of course, would have brought the whole trend below the base line. Which year or period seems fairer? (See Fig. 4-20 and Table 4-5.)

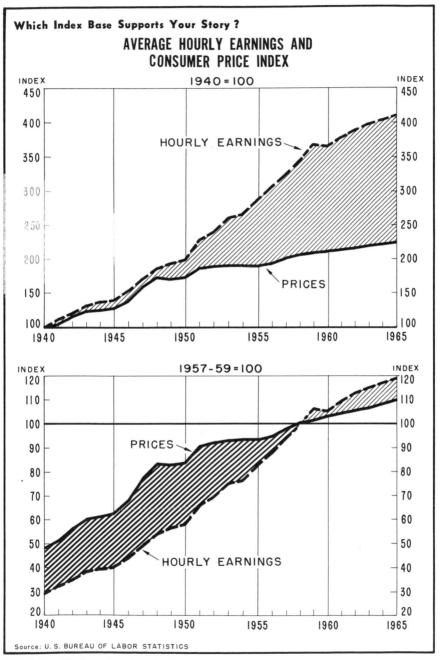

Which Index Base Supports Your Story ?

AVERAGE HOURLY EARNINGS AND
CONSUMER PRICE INDEX

Source: U. S. BUREAU OF LABOR STATISTICS

FIG. 4-20   Effect of changing the base year.

TABLE 4-5   *Index of Average Hourly Earnings and Consumer Price Index*

Year	1940 = 100		1957–1959 = 100	
	Avg. hourly earnings	*Consumer Price Index*	*Avg. hourly earnings*	*Consumer Price Index*
1940	*100.0*	*100.0*	29.0	48.8
1941	111.5	105.1	32.3	51.3
1942	120.6	116.4	34.9	56.8
1943	132.2	123.6	38.3	60.3
1944	137.1	125.6	39.7	61.3
1945	139.7	128.5	40.5	62.7
1946	151.8	139.3	43.9	68.0
1947	170.5	159.4	49.4	77.8
1948	187.2	171.7	54.2	83.8
1949	195.0	170.1	56.5	83.0
1950	200.4	171.7	58.1	83.8
1951	227.5	185.5	65.9	90.5
1952	239.3	189.5	69.3	92.5
1953	259.5	191.0	75.2	93.2
1954	264.2	191.8	76.5	93.6
1955	285.5	191.2	82.7	93.3
1956	304.5	194.1	88.2	94.7
1957	323.5	200.8	*93.7*	*98.0*
1958	344.8	206.4	*99.9*	*100.7*
1959	367.3	208.0	*106.4*	*101.5*
1960	364.9	211.3	105.7	103.1
1961	379.1	213.5	109.8	104.2
1962	389.8	216.0	112.9	105.4
1963	398.1	218.6	115.1	106.7
1964°	404.0	221.5°	117.0	108.1°
1965	410.0	225.2	118.8	109.9

° New series beginning January, 1964.

Note: Hourly earnings assumed indexes.

SOURCE: Consumer Price Index, U.S. Department of Labor, Bureau of Labor Statistics.

THE INDEX BASE LINE

Opinions differ concerning the importance of starting the scale of an index chart from zero.

If a multiple-base graph such as is found in business charts is made (see A, Fig. 4-21), the grid may be drawn only as large as is necessary to accommodate the maximum and minimum variations of trends. The viewers of this type of chart are usually familiar with this layout and have no difficulty in interpreting it.

The two charts in B, Fig. 4-21, show the effect on the trends produced by drawing the grid from zero and by using only that part of the scale to accommodate the high and low points of the trends. The latter layout is more commonly used. In either case the chart should accent the 100 base line.

Occasionally the amount of space allotted the chart may be the deciding factor in determining whether or not a zero line should be used. If the trends are high above the 100 base line or too similar to be read clearly when the layout begins with zero, start the chart at the first scale unit that will cover the lowest figure in the data. However, the 100 base line must appear on the chart to show the relationship of the data.

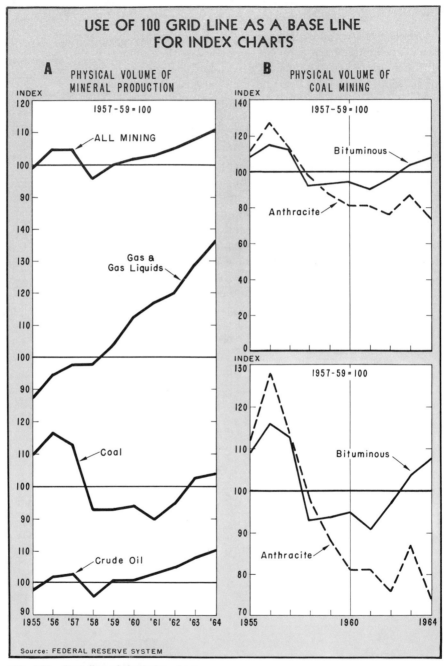

FIG. 4-21   Base line of the index chart.

COMPARING PERIODS OF TIME

Periods of time may be compared by using two *time scales*. Here, as in the multiple-amount-scale chart (see Fig. 4-13), particular care must be taken to identify the time scale with its corresponding trend. This is accomplished by using different styles of lettering or colors.

Note in Fig. 4-22 that both the time scale and labels relating to World War I are slanted, whereas those concerning World War II are vertical. The chart, comparing the indexes of wholesale prices in World War I and World War II, shows how prices shot up after each war (see Table 4-6).

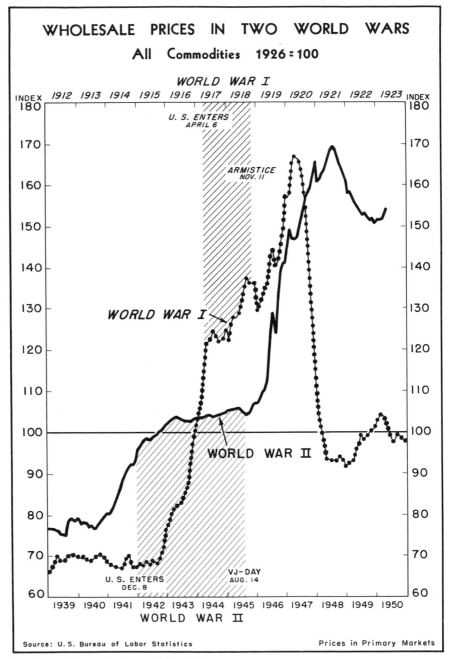

FIG. 4-22 Comparing two periods of time.

TABLE 4-6   *Wholesale Prices° in Two World Wars, All Commodities*
(*Index Numbers 1926 = 100*)
  World War I

Months	1912	1913	1914	1915	1916	1917	1918	1919	1920	1921	1922	1923
Jan.	66.0	70.3	68.6	68.1	77.0	102.1	125.0	134.4	157.7	114.0	91.4	102.0
Feb.	66.7	69.8	68.3	68.6	78.5	104.5	122.7	129.8	157.1	104.9	92.9	103.3
Mar.	67.5	69.9	68.0	68.2	80.4	107.7	126.4	131.3	158.6	102.4	92.8	104.5
Apr.	69.7	69.7	67.6	68.7	81.7	114.1	128.3	133.0	165.5	98.9	93.2	103.9
May	70.0	68.9	67.4	69.0	82.5	120.7	128.1	135.3	167.2	96.2	96.1	101.9
June	69.0	69.0	67.4	68.3	82.9	122.0	129.0	135.6	166.5	93.4	96.3	100.3
July	68.9	69.5	67.3	69.3	83.4	123.0	132.0	141.1	165.8	93.4	99.4	98.4
Aug.	69.7	69.7	69.6	68.6	85.1	124.8	134.3	144.3	161.4	93.5	98.6	97.8
Sept.	70.5	70.6	70.2	68.3	86.9	123.5	137.5	141.1	155.2	93.4	99.3	99.7
Oct.	70.8	70.4	68.0	70.2	91.1	122.2	136.3	141.6	144.2	94.1	99.6	99.4
Nov.	70.2	70.1	67.5	71.7	97.4	122.8	136.3	144.5	133.4	94.2	100.5	98.4
Dec.	70.1	69.1	67.3	74.0	99.2	122.9	136.3	150.5	120.7	92.9	100.7	98.1

  World War II

Months	1939	1940	1941	1942	1943	1944	1945	1946	1947	1948	1949	1950
Jan.	76.9	79.4	80.8	96.0	101.9	103.3	104.9	107.1	141.5	165.7	160.6	151.5
Feb.	76.9	78.7	80.6	96.7	102.5	103.6	105.2	107.7	144.5	160.9	158.1	152.7
Mar.	76.7	78.4	81.5	97.6	103.4	103.8	105.3	108.9	149.5	161.4	158.4	152.7
Apr.	76.2	78.6	83.2	98.7	103.7	103.9	105.7	110.2	147.7	162.8	156.9	152.9
May	76.2	78.4	84.9	98.8	104.1	104.0	106.0	111.0	147.1	163.9	155.7	155.9
June	75.6	77.5	87.1	98.6	103.8	104.3	106.1	112.9	147.6	166.2	154.5	
July	75.4	77.7	88.8	98.7	103.2	104.1	105.9	124.7	150.6	168.7	153.6	
Aug.	75.0	77.4	90.3	99.2	103.1	103.9	105.7	129.1	153.6	169.5	153.0	
Sept.	79.1	78.0	91.8	99.6	103.1	104.0	105.2	124.0	157.4	168.7	153.6	
Oct.	79.4	78.7	92.4	100.0	103.0	104.1	105.9	134.1	158.5	165.2	152.2	
Nov.	79.2	76.9	92.5	100.3	102.9	104.4	106.8	139.7	159.7	164.0	151.6	
Dec.	79.2	80.0	93.6	101.0	103.2	104.7	107.1	140.9	163.2	162.4	151.9	

° Prices in primary markets.
SOURCE: U.S. Department of Labor, Bureau of Labor Statistics.

HISTORICAL NOTES

Further interest may be added to a trend chart by noting historical or economic events at the dates they occur. A political touch is added to the chart in Fig. 4-23 by noting presidential terms of office.

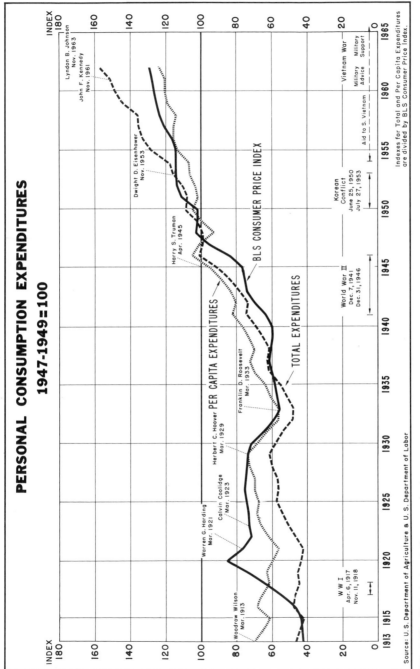

PERSONAL CONSUMPTION EXPENDITURES
1947-1949=100

FIG. 4-23 Historical notations on chart.

STEP CHARTS

The line chart is drawn in the step or staircase format (Fig. 4-24):

1. *When showing abrupt fluctuations in data.* In chart *B* of Fig. 4-24, the steepness of the trend showing work stoppages in 1952 and 1959 would be read less accurately if inked as a curve chart.

2. *When presenting irregular periods of time,* such as daily price changes or similar data. Figure 4-24*C* shows, by specified dates, the initial margin requirements for an investor who wishes to buy securities. In November, 1963, the margin was raised from 50 to 70 percent. This means that the investor, using credit to buy listed securities, is required to put up 70 percent, the balance being advanced by the broker.

Note that the years are labeled in the space, as dates change during that period of time. If exact dates are essential, make a table of changes to go with the chart as a reference.

3. *When depicting frequency distribution.* In chart *A*, Fig. 4-24, the relative size of the class intervals is readily discerned. The shading of the first and last group calls attention to the fact that those intervals are *under* and *over* the regular limits.

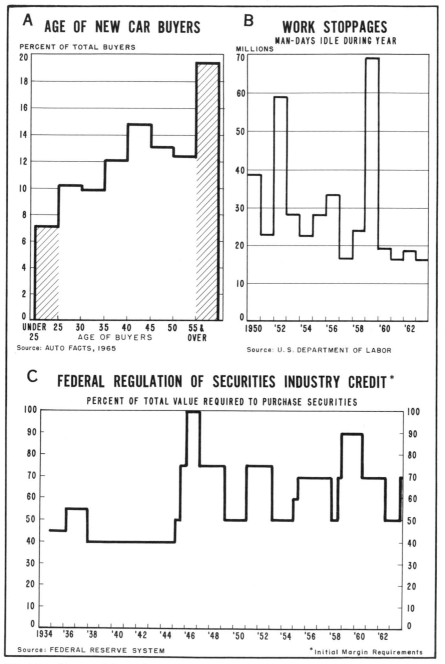

A AGE OF NEW CAR BUYERS

PERCENT OF TOTAL BUYERS

Source: AUTO FACTS, 1965

B WORK STOPPAGES
MAN-DAYS IDLE DURING YEAR

MILLIONS

Source: U. S. DEPARTMENT OF LABOR

C FEDERAL REGULATION OF SECURITIES INDUSTRY CREDIT*

PERCENT OF TOTAL VALUE REQUIRED TO PURCHASE SECURITIES

Source: FEDERAL RESERVE SYSTEM   *Initial Margin Requirements

FIG. 4-24   Step or staircase layouts.

FREQUENCY-DISTRIBUTION CHARTS

Frequency-distribution charts are commonly plotted in step or staircase graphic form. Generally the person making the step chart is furnished the data in class groupings for the layout. The groupings or intervals, having been chosen from the array of raw data, show how many classes there are and what class limits should be used.

The horizontal scale controls the size of each class interval. The vertical scale shows the number of items in that class. This scale, when arithmetic, should always begin at zero. Logarithmic scales may be used on both horizontal and vertical grids.

Common practice in presenting frequency-distribution charts is to break the frequency scale. The complete extent of the distribution is not shown, as the extreme limits are grouped. When the step format calls for such *open ends, under* and *over* the regular limits, shading them will call attention to this fact (see A in Fig. 4-24).

When possible, make all class intervals the same width. Groupings should be definite and should not overlap when labeled. Do not use 0–5, 5–10, 10–15, 15–20. This leaves one to wonder in which group 5, 10, and 15 belong. Rather, label the intervals this way: "under 5," "5 and under 10," etc.; or "5 to less than 10"; or "0–4.9," "5–9.9." This labeling should be directly under the vertical ruling.

When the class intervals are *unequal* in the frequency distribution, numerical adjustments must be made for their plotting. Thus, in the step chart in Fig. 4-25 and the curve chart in Fig. 4-27, adjustments were made by dividing the frequencies of the class "$6,000 to $7,499" by 1.5 units, the space the class covers, and plotting $190.70; the class of "$7,500 to $9,999" by 2.5 units; and the class of "$10,000 to $14,999" by 5 units. The numerals in italics on Table 4-7 are the adjusted data plotted. As the "$15,000-and-over" interval was extreme, it was not drafted. See Fig. 4-26 for making adjustments when plotting unequal class intervals.

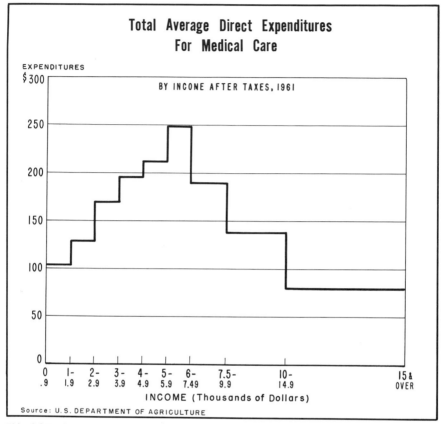

FIG. 4-25 Step chart for frequency distribution data.

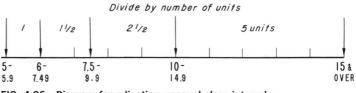

FIG. 4-26   Diagram for adjusting unequal class intervals.

TABLE 4-7   *Average Expenditures for Medical Care and Amounts Received without Expenditure (By Income after Taxes, 1961)*

Expenditures, dollars	Total direct expenditures	Prepaid care	Free care
Under 1,000	105	21	28
1,000–1,999	131	30	42
2,000–2,999	171	59	30
3,000–3,999	197	76	31
4,000–4,999	213	85	29
5,000–5,999	248	98	34
6,000–7,499	286 (*190.7*)	113 (*75.3*)	39 (*26.0*)
7,500–9,999	349 (*139.6*)	126 (*50.4*)	32 (*12.8*)
10,000–14,999	438 (*87.6*)	151 (*30.2*)	38 (*7.6*)
15,000 and over	706	178	33

Note: Preliminary data for 1961. Numerals in italics are amounts plotted.

SOURCE: Jean L. Pennock, U.S. Department of Agriculture, *Family Expenditures for Medical Care,* November, 1965.

As a rule, in the step chart only one series of data is plotted, because the vertical rulings of the steps may coincide and more than one line would be confusing and hard to follow. For multifrequency curves, line charts are drawn. The chart in Fig. 4-27 is plotted at midclass intervals. The data were numerically adjusted where needed.

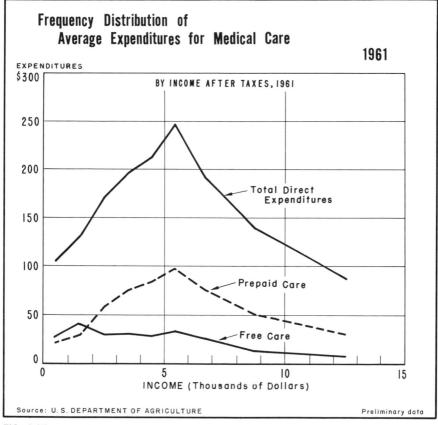

FIG. 4-27   **Use of curves for more than one frequency.**

THE CUMULATIVE-FREQUENCY CHART

A cumulative-frequency chart is depicted in Fig. 4-28. It shows the cumulative number of drivers and their accident experience by age groups for the year 1963. This type of chart is used sparingly for popular presentation, as it could easily be misread. For plotting and preparing data for cumulative charts see Fig. 4-33 and Table 4-8.

Not all types of frequency-distribution charts that are used for statistical analysis are shown. Only those of more popular appeal are drafted here for their simplicity.

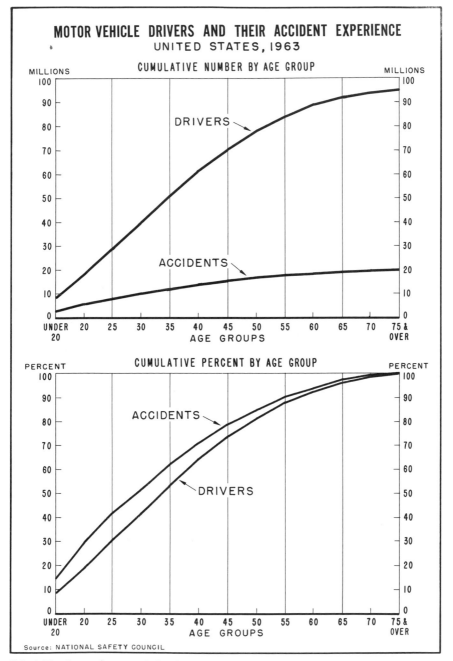

FIG. 4-28 Comparing cumulative frequency curves.

THE SHADED STEP CHART

Shading or crosshatching the surface of the step frequency chart, as in Fig. 4-29, accents the overall picture. The first and last intervals were given heavier shading in order to call special attention to the fact that the end intervals, those under 20 years and those 75 and over, were grouped.

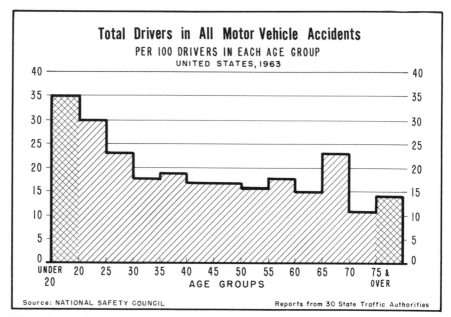

FIG. 4-29   Shading the step frequency chart.

THE HISTOGRAM

For popular presentation the histogram or column frequency diagram is used in preference to the step or polygon-curve charts. It is easier to read, as the individual classes stand out more clearly. Should the intervals be unequal, the width of the columns should be numerically adjusted similar to Fig. 4-26. In this type of chart the frequency amount is represented by the *area* of the column (see Fig. 4-30). This is not to be confused with the time-series connected-column chart (see Fig. 6-7).

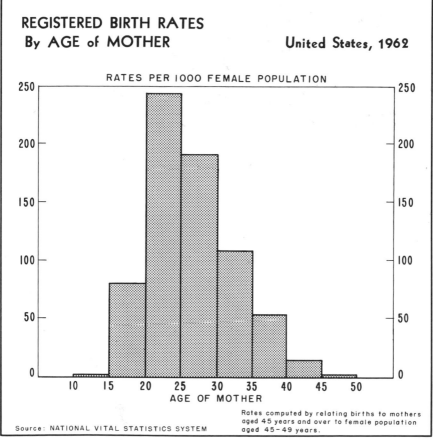

FIG. 4-30   The histogram.

In Fig. 4-31, the individual age of passenger cars in use is represented by columns with the *open end* shaded.

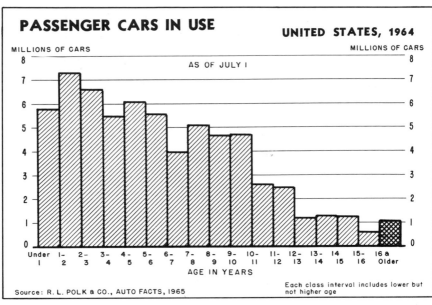

FIG. 4-31   Shading the open-end histogram.

Monthly Passenger Car Production
UNITED STATES, 1964

MILLIONS OF CARS

CUMULATIVE

Source: AUTOMOBILE MANUFACTURERS ASSOCIATION

FIG. 4-32 Plotting from a cumulative table.

TABLE 4-8   *Monthly Passenger-car Production, United States, 1964*

Month	Monthly data	Cumulative data for plotting
Jan.	745,835	745,835
Feb.	675,581	1,421,416
Mar.	723,811	2,145,227
Apr.	786,824	2,932,051
May	726,007	3,658,058
June	777,595	4,435,653
July	587,292	5,022,945
Aug.	190,159	5,213,104
Sept.	573,420	5,786,524
Oct.	411,501	6,198,025
Nov.	680,835	6,878,860
Dec.	866,632	7,745,492

SOURCE: *Auto Facts*, 1965, p. 9.

THE CUMULATIVE CURVE

The cumulative-curve chart is used when the primary interest is in the cumulative pattern over a period of time. The chart in Fig. 4-33 shows the cumulative number of housing units started from 1945 through 1964.

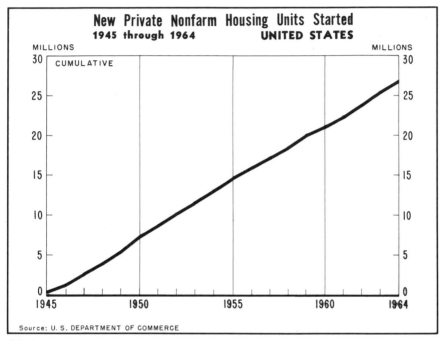

New Private Nonfarm Housing Units Started
1945 through 1964   **UNITED STATES**

Source: U. S. DEPARTMENT OF COMMERCE

FIG. 4-33   The cumulative-curve chart.

To plot cumulative data a special table should be made for the draftsman. It is not his responsibility to add the data. Such a table should be labeled prominently, *for plotting,* so that it may not be misused at a later date (see Fig. 4-32 and Table 4-8).

The cumulative curve can be used in conjunction with daily, weekly, or monthly data. The chart in Fig. 4-34 was made during World War I by the U.S. Food Administration. It shows the weekly exports of corn by using columns, while the cumulative amount is shown by the curves.

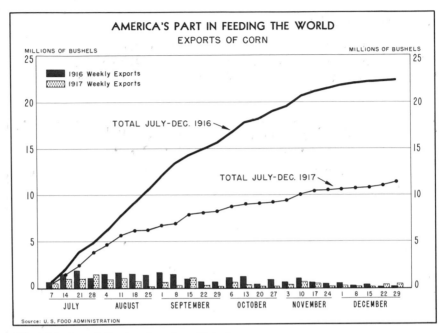

FIG. 4-34   Cumulative trends and weekly columns.

A PROGRESS REPORT

Figure 4-35 depicts the progress in a production program. The upper chart plots the actual cumulated deliveries of planes against the number scheduled to be delivered by certain dates. The lower chart uses the subdivided connected columns to record the number of monthly deliveries to each of the two zones. Thus the two charts picture the monthly progress and the cumulated production in relation to the ultimate goal.

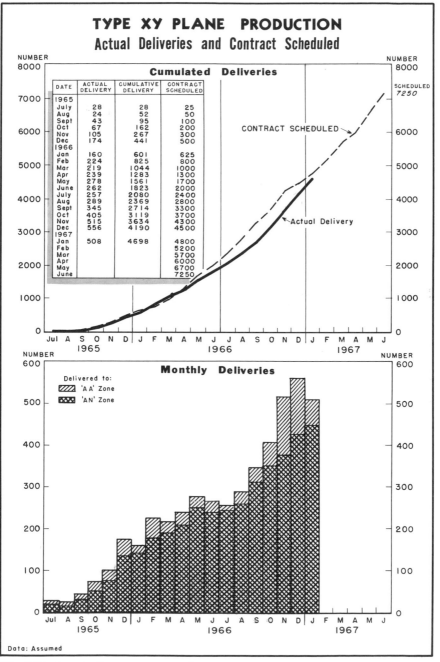

TYPE XY PLANE PRODUCTION
Actual Deliveries and Contract Scheduled

Cumulated Deliveries

DATE	ACTUAL DELIVERY	CUMULATIVE DELIVERY	CONTRACT SCHEDULED
1965			
July	28	28	25
Aug	24	52	50
Sept	43	95	100
Oct	67	162	200
Nov	105	267	300
Dec	174	441	500
1966			
Jan	160	601	625
Feb	224	825	800
Mar	219	1044	1000
Apr	239	1283	1300
May	278	1561	1700
June	262	1823	2000
July	257	2080	2400
Aug	289	2369	2800
Sept	345	2714	3300
Oct	405	3119	3700
Nov	515	3634	4300
Dec	556	4190	4500
1967			
Jan	508	4698	4800
Feb			5200
Mar			5700
Apr			6000
May			6700
June			7250

CONTRACT SCHEDULED

Actual Delivery

SCHEDULED 7250

Monthly Deliveries

Delivered to:
'A A' Zone
'A N' Zone

Data: Assumed

FIG. 4-35   A production progress report.

THE LOGARITHMIC CHART

The value of the logarithmic chart is recognized now more than in the past for popular presentations. Unlike the arithmetic chart which shows the *amount of change* in a trend, the logarithmic chart shows the *rate of change* (see Fig. 4-36).

For example, let us assume that a chain-store manager wishes to compare the rate of growth in sales between two stores. Store A is in a large city, and store B is in a new suburban area. In the charts, Fig. 4-36, when the sales are plotted on an arithmetic scale, store A's sales appear to have advanced rapidly, while the sales in store B appear to be gradual. However, when the data are plotted on a logarithmic or ratio scale, the *rate of change* in sales shows an almost identical rate of increase for both stores (see Table 4-9).

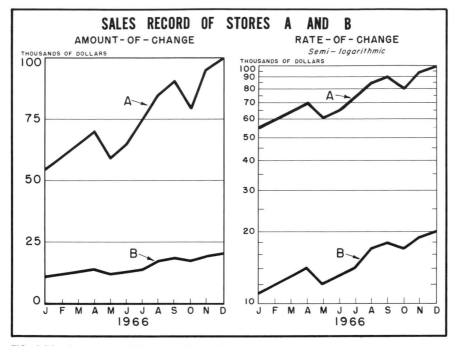

FIG. 4-36 Comparing arithmetic and logarithmic scales.

TABLE 4-9   *Sales Record*

Month	Store A	Store B
Jan.	$ 55,000	$11,000
Feb.	60,000	12,000
Mar.	65,000	13,000
Apr.	70,000	14,000
May	60,000	12,000
June	65,000	13,000
July	75,000	14,000
Aug.	85,000	16,500
Sept.	90,000	18,000
Oct.	80,000	16,500
Nov.	95,000	19,000
Dec.	100,000	20,000

Note: Data assumed.

THE LOGARITHMIC SCALE

The visual difference in reading the amount curve and the logarithmic curve is that in the graph with the arithmetic scale, the amounts are read from *zero* or a *base* line. The rate of change on a logarithmic chart is determined by the *slope* of the trend line. There is no zero on a logarithmic chart (see Fig. 4-37).

To read the curves correctly on the log chart, it must be understood that the steepness or slope of the lines connecting the plotted points indicates the *rate of change*; that is, the steeper the rise or fall of these lines, the greater the ratio of increase or decrease.

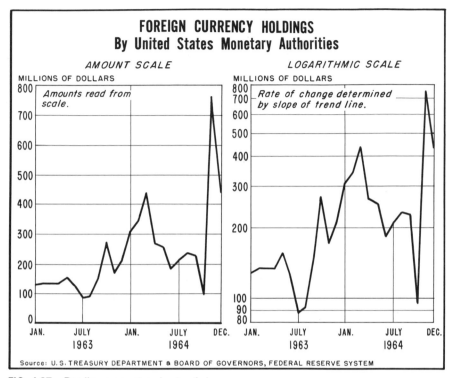

FIG. 4-37   Reading amount and rate-of-change curves.

CONSTRUCTING THE LOGARITHMIC SCALE

It is not necessary to convert arithmetic data into logarithms mathematically or to use a logarithmic table for plotting. Semilogarithmic and full-logarithmic printed sheets are obtainable in various number of cycles from art and drafting supply stores. Arithmetic data can be plotted directly on them. If the chart is to be enlarged on bristol board, the grid layout can be made by line extension using the printed logarithmic cycles as a guide (see Fig. 4-38).

There is also a flat, beveled, statistician's 12-in. scale that is handy and meets the needs of desk-size charts. It carries five complete logarithmic scales: 4.17, 6.25, 10, 12.5, and 25 cm; the metric scale, 30 cm reading in millimeters; and one 12-in. scale, 40 to the inch.

Figure 4-39 shows how to construct a cycle to fit a given space by cutting a cycle from log paper and extending the divisions. This layout can also be used for marking off a plotting scale.

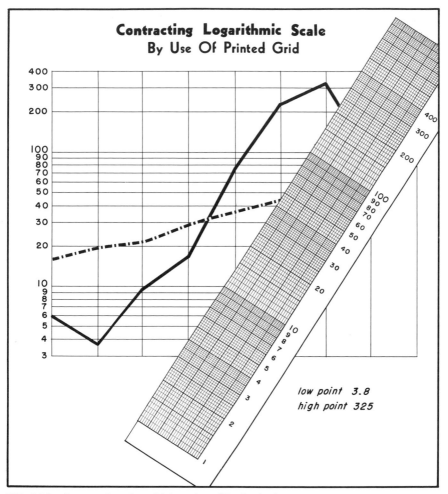

FIG. 4-38   Constructing the grid for a logarithmic chart.

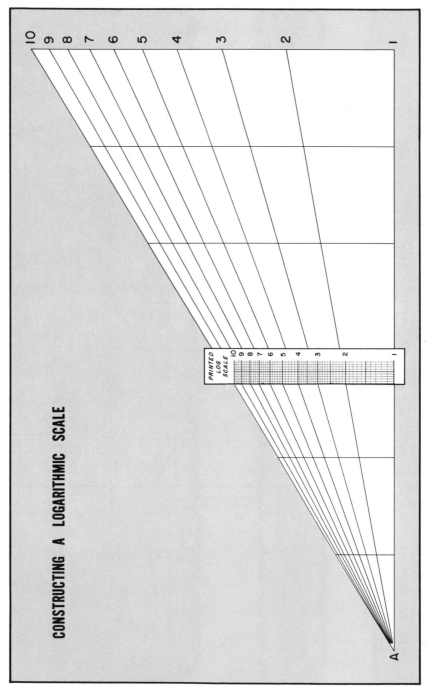

FIG. 4-39 Log scale pattern made by line extension.

THE PLOTTING SCALE

A plotting scale is a slip of stiff paper that is marked off into a breakdown of a scale unit of a chart in order to correctly locate the points when plotting. Make it a full cycle, 1 to 10. It may be moved from cycle to cycle when plotting the data. (See Fig. 4-39 for scale layout.)

SELECTING THE LOG SCALE

The logarithmic chart may consist of several cycles (decks, spans, or phases) beginning with any number greater than zero. The value placed at the top of the cycle will be ten times that at the bottom of the cycle. Figure 4-40 shows a few selected scales. These scales may be on the horizontal or vertical grid for a semilogarithmic chart or on both grids in a full log layout.

The grid with the vertical ruling carrying the logarithmic scale and the horizontal ruling carrying the arithmetic scale denoting time is the most common. Charts of this type are referred to as *semilogarithmic* charts. In this text the term *logarithmic* is used as a general term for all charts shown with a log scale.

If the data do not warrant a full cycle, only part of a cycle may be drawn, that is, enough to accommodate the high and low points. The chart in Fig. 4-41 required a whole cycle, but only part of the lower and upper cycles, to show the rate of change in private construction activity.

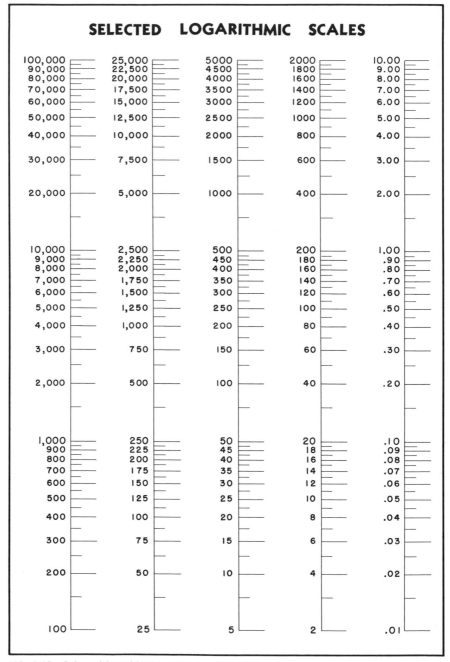

FIG. 4-40   Selected logarithmic scale units.

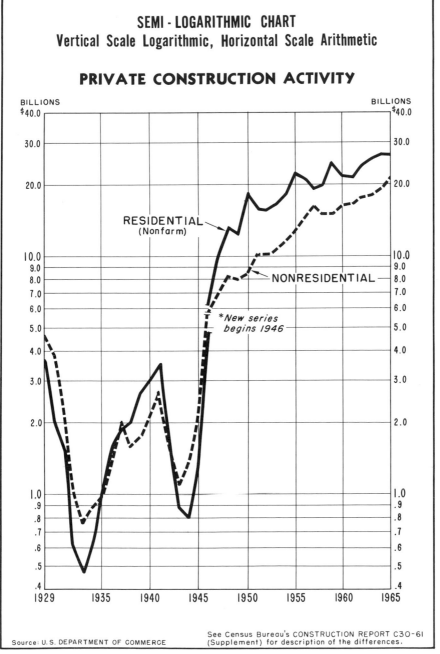

SEMI - LOGARITHMIC CHART
Vertical Scale Logarithmic, Horizontal Scale Arithmetic

PRIVATE CONSTRUCTION ACTIVITY

BILLIONS
$40.0

RESIDENTIAL
(Nonfarm)

NONRESIDENTIAL

*New series
begins 1946

BILLIONS
$40.0

Source: U.S. DEPARTMENT OF COMMERCE

See Census Bureau's CONSTRUCTION REPORT C30-61
(Supplement) for description of the differences.

FIG. 4-41   Using part of a logarithmic cycle.

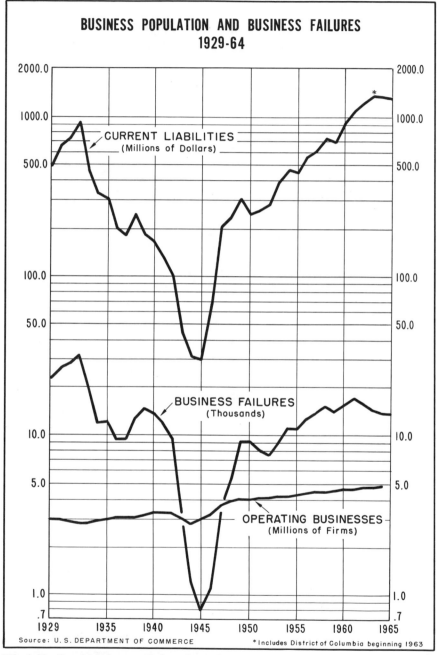

FIG. 4-42   Trend labels carry their scale captions.

PLOTTING UNLIKE CATEGORIES

One of the many uses of the logarithmic chart is to compare the *rate of change* of *unlike* categories. Hence, several curves can be plotted on the same graph and their ratios studied. It will be noted that in Fig. 4-42 each curve label carries its own scale caption, that is, "millions of dollars," "thousands," and "millions of firms." No caption appears over the log scale.

The same is true in Fig. 4-43, where the rate of change of both amounts and indexes are plotted. If it is not obvious at first glance that the scale is logarithmic, it is wise to note this on the chart so that the scale will not be mistaken for an amount scale.

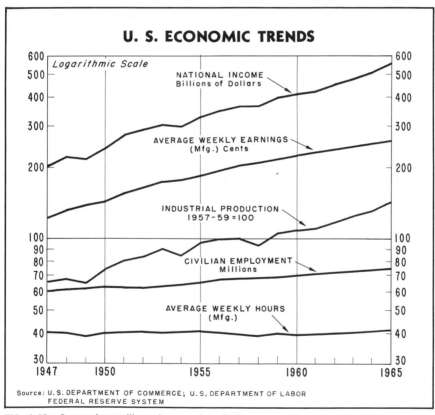

FIG. 4-43 Comparing unlike units on a log chart.

WHEN NOT TO USE THE LOG CHART

The logarithmic chart should not be used to bring together curves of widely different magnitude in order to compare their *amounts* more closely. This is a common error. The log chart would still show the *rate* of change and not the *amount* of change. Both of the charts in Fig. 4-44 are correct for their purposes, but each shows a different aspect of the same data.

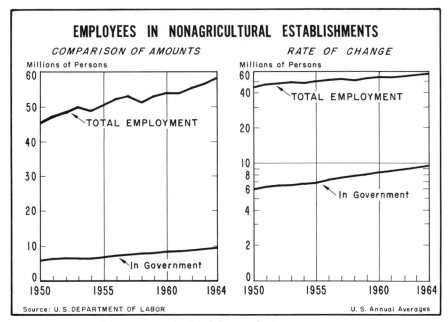

FIG. 4-44   Comparing amount and rate-of-change charts.

THE FAN CHART

The fan chart, so called because of its format, usually shows the percentage change or the index increase or decrease of items from one selected base date to another period of time. This form of chart has the advantage over a table in that the amount of change is visually shown in numerical order. The chart in Fig. 4-45 depicts the percentage increase and decrease in United States agriculture exports. Fats, oils, and greases were high, while cottonseed and soybean oils decreased since 1963.

Figure 4-46 compares the cost of living abroad in selected cities for two years. From the indexes it can be seen that Paris was the most costly in 1962, when based on New York cost of living, but in 1964 Tokyo was highest. Rio de Janeiro was the same as New York in 1962 and rose slightly in 1964.

The use of shading in Fig. 4-47 accents, for three decades, the *decrease* of population in the rural farm areas in Washington County, Maryland.

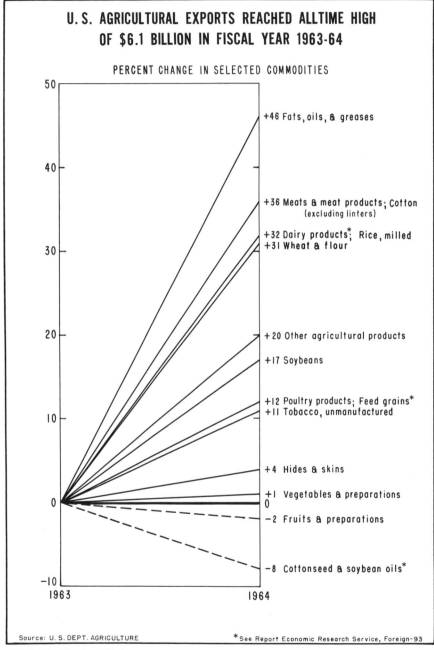

U. S. AGRICULTURAL EXPORTS REACHED ALLTIME HIGH OF $6.1 BILLION IN FISCAL YEAR 1963-64

PERCENT CHANGE IN SELECTED COMMODITIES

+46 Fats, oils, & greases

+36 Meats & meat products; Cotton
(excluding linters)

+32 Dairy products*; Rice, milled
+31 Wheat & flour

+20 Other agricultural products

+17 Soybeans

+12 Poultry products; Feed grains*
+11 Tobacco, unmanufactured

+4 Hides & skins

+1 Vegetables & preparations
0
-2 Fruits & preparations

-8 Cottonseed & soybean oils*

1963   1964

Source: U. S. DEPT. AGRICULTURE   *See Report Economic Research Service, Foreign-93

FIG. 4-45   The fan chart.

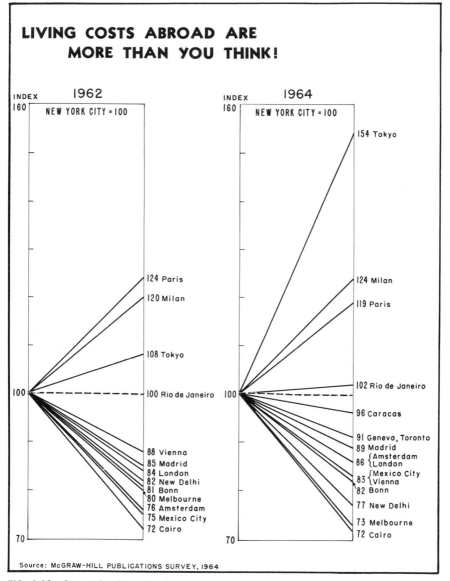

FIG. 4-46 Comparing items for two years by fan charts.

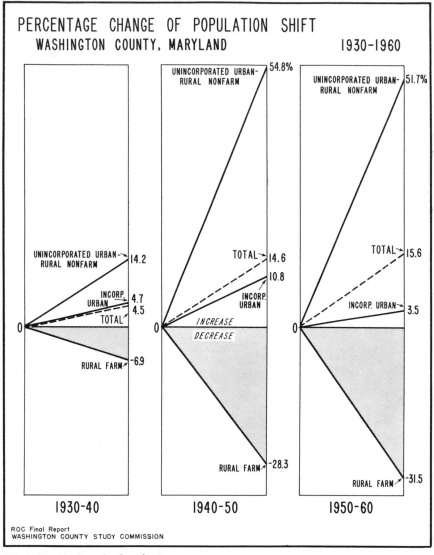

PERCENTAGE CHANGE OF POPULATION SHIFT
WASHINGTON COUNTY, MARYLAND   1930-1960

UNINCORPORATED URBAN-
RURAL NONFARM   54.8%

UNINCORPORATED URBAN-
RURAL NONFARM   51.7%

UNINCORPORATED URBAN-
RURAL NONFARM   14.2

TOTAL   14.6

TOTAL   15.6

INCORP.   4.7
URBAN
4.5

10.8

INCORP.
URBAN

INCORP. URBAN   3.5

TOTAL

0   0   0

INCREASE

DECREASE

RURAL FARM   -6.9

RURAL FARM   -28.3

RURAL FARM   -31.5

1930-40   1940-50   1950-60

ROC Final Report
WASHINGTON COUNTY STUDY COMMISSION

FIG. 4-47   Shading the fan chart.

FIVE

The Surface Chart

The surface chart, also known as the band or stratum chart, should be used:

1. *When the magnitude of a trend is to be emphasized, as in a simple surface chart (see Fig. 5-1)*

2. *When a general cumulative picture of components of a total trend is to be shown (see Fig. 5-7)*

3. *When some portion of a chart is to be accented for a specific purpose, as the zone chart in Fig. 5-13*

THE SIMPLE SURFACE CHART

The simple surface chart depicts a single trend-line chart with shading, crosshatching, photographs, or illustrations filling in the area between the trend and base lines. This shading, as seen in Fig. 5-1, tends to give a silhouette effect which emphasizes the overall picture of the trend.

141

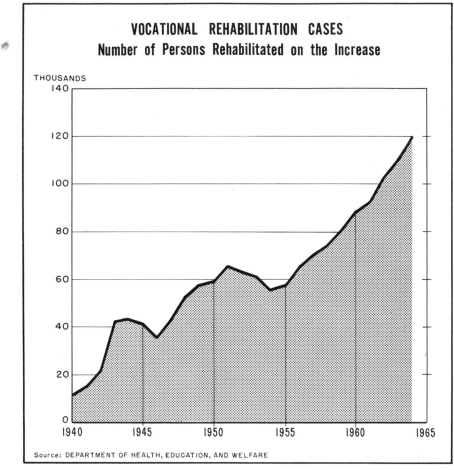

FIG. 5-1   The simple surface chart.

THE PHOTOSURFACE

Photographs may be used instead of shading patterns to cover the surface below the trend line. The photosurface in Fig. 5-2 was made by first tracing the outlines of the trend, base line, and connecting vertical grids of the finished inked chart. This tracing was then laid over the photograph. The portion of the picture most suitable for the photosurface was marked, cut out, and applied to the original chart with rubber cement. Dry photomounting or spray adhesives may be used.

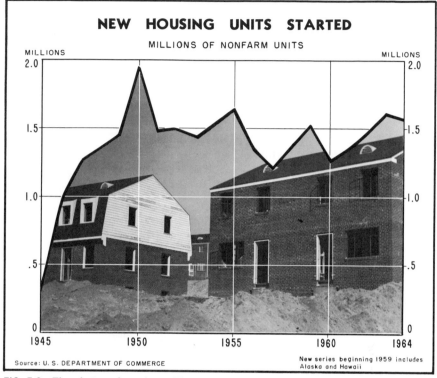

NEW HOUSING UNITS STARTED

MILLIONS OF NONFARM UNITS

Source: U. S. DEPARTMENT OF COMMERCE

New series beginning 1959 includes Alaska and Hawaii

FIG. 5-2   The photosurface chart. (Photo courtesy of Albert Spear.)

An office studio should have a dry-mounting press if there is much mounting to be done. Such a press is electrically operated and applies heat and pressure speedily. It handles a wide variety of materials for various types of presentations. Using laminating film will protect display materials and give them long life.

Protect your photographs from mars and scratches. Do not write heavily on the backs of them; the pressure of the pen or pencil will show through. Paper clips or staples will also deface them. Cover the surface with a lightweight paper or tissue. Attach the tissue to the back of the illustration with tape or rubber cement.

ILLUSTRATIONS AS A SURFACE

Illustrations may lend themselves to the format of the surface chart as well as photographs (see Fig. 5-3). Rendered in pen and ink, airbrush, or wash drawings, they give a more personal appeal than stock photographs.

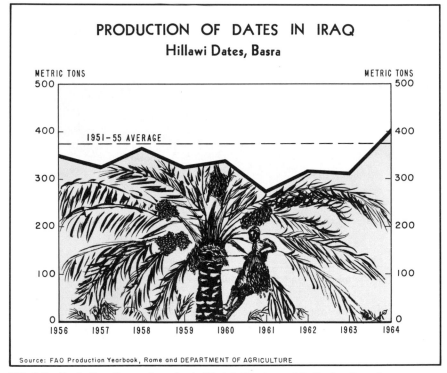

PRODUCTION OF DATES IN IRAQ
Hillawi Dates, Basra

METRIC TONS

METRIC TONS

1951–55 AVERAGE

Source: FAO Production Yearbook, Rome and DEPARTMENT OF AGRICULTURE

FIG. 5-3   Illustrating the surface chart. (Sketch Courtesy of Katherine Spear.)

OPTICAL ILLUSIONS WITH SHADING

Be careful when using shading to silhouette a trend. You may unintentionally be creating an optical illusion and thus spoiling the objective of your chart. Part *A* in Fig. 5-4 emphasizes the trend by using black below the trend line, whereas the black shading in part *B*, above the same trend line, seems to reduce the amount of the plotting. This illusion often occurs when color is used to *dress up* a chart.

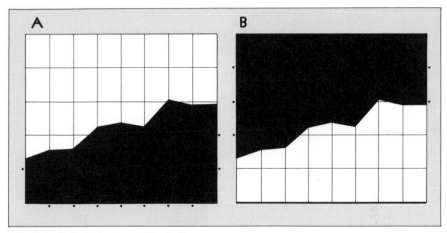

FIG. 5-4   Optical illusions with shading.

THE ZERO BASE LINE

When surface charts are for popular presentation, the amount scale should always be plotted from the zero base line. A broken scale distorts the visual image and overemphasizes the difference in amounts (see Fig. 5-5).

As an exception, the broken scale will appear in business charts, as a specialized audience, familiar with this format, knows how to interpret them.

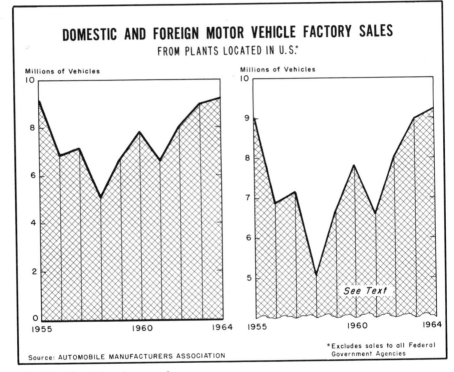

FIG. 5-5   Use full scale on surface.

PLOT ON FIRST VERTICAL GRID

It is advisable to start the plottings of a chart on the first vertical grid and identify it. A space left at the beginning of the plotted trend may cause confusion in reading the time period. This is particularly noticeable in monthly plotting of data.

In Fig. 5-6 both charts begin in March, 1964. There is no question about the time period in chart *A*, while in chart *B* the ticks must be counted off to identify the months.

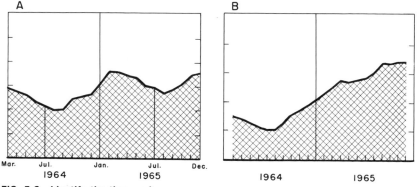

FIG. 5-6   Identify the time scale.

THE SUBDIVIDED-SURFACE CHART

The subdivided-surface chart (see Fig. 5-7) contains a series of bands or strata depicting the components of a total trend or 100 percent band chart. This type of chart gives only a general picture and should not be used where changes in the movement of trends are abrupt or where accurate reading of a component is of paramount importance.

The width of each band is read from the band plotted below it and not from zero. Hence, the first band which is plotted from the base line is more accurately read.

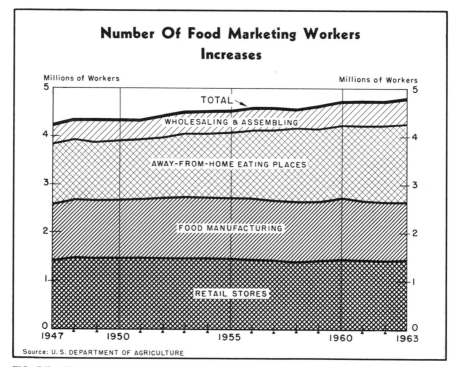

FIG. 5-7   Plotting the band chart.

PLOTTING THE BANDS

Several things must be considered when plotting the subdivided-surface chart:

1. *The movement of the trends.* To get a true picture of the data to be plotted, it is advisable to first plot the trends on cross-hatched paper. This gives the opportunity of studying trend movements and helps in the selection of plotting sequence of the bands (see Fig. 5-8 and Table 5-1A).

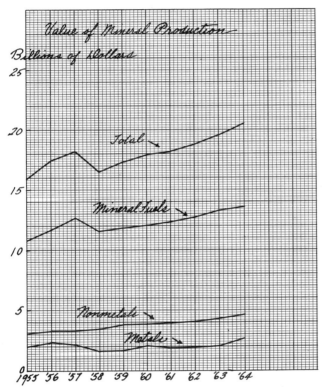

FIG. 5-8   Rough layout for movement of trend.

TABLE 5-1A   *Value of Mineral Production (Millions of Dollars)*
Original table for plotting Fig. 5-8

Year	Mineral fuels	Nonmetals	Metals	Total
1955	10,780	3,076	2,055	15,911
1956	11,741	3,391	2,358	17,490
1957	12,709	3,387	2,137	18,233
1958	11,589	3,466	1,594	16,649
1959	11,950	3,861	1,570	17,381
1960	12,142	3,868	2,022	18,032
1961	12,357	3,946	1,927	18,230
1962	12,784	4,117	1,937	18,838
1963	13,296	4,318	2,006	19,620
1964	13,585	4,622	2,265	20,472

Note: Includes Alaska and Hawaii.
SOURCE: U.S. Department of Interior.

2. *The sequence of bands.* Plottings should cumulate beginning with those trends of least movement, as abrupt plotted points will disturb the contours of the bands plotted above them. This is apt to cause an optical distortion in the width of the bands.

In the simple chart in Fig. 5-9, the smoothness of the trends was the deciding factor for their order. "Nonmetals" had the least movement and was plotted first. "Metals" was added to it, while "Mineral Fuels," having a peak in 1957 and a steeper rise in the following years, was added as the third band (see Fig. 5-9 and Table 5-1*B*).

While the chart may visually appear better if the bands are plotted progressively according to width and starting with the widest band, this is not always feasible.

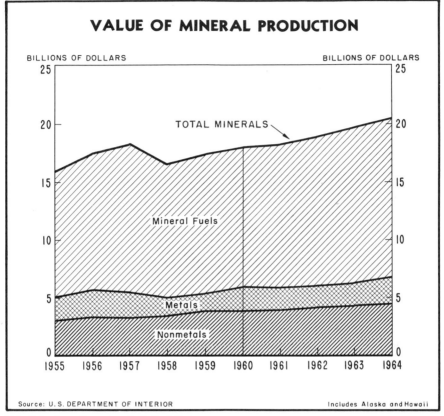

VALUE OF MINERAL PRODUCTION

BILLIONS OF DOLLARS   BILLIONS OF DOLLARS

TOTAL MINERALS

Mineral Fuels

Metals

Nonmetals

Source: U.S. DEPARTMENT OF INTERIOR   Includes Alaska and Hawaii

FIG. 5-9   Smoothest trend plotted first.

TABLE 5-1B   *Value of Mineral Production (Millions of Dollars)*
Table 5-1A cumulated for plotting Fig. 5-9

Year	Nonmetals	+	Metals	+	Mineral fuels	=	Total minerals
1955	3,076		5,131				15,911
1956	3,391		5,749				17,490
1957	3,387		5,524				18,233
1958	3,466		5,060				16,649
1959	3,861		5,431				17,381
1960	3,868		5,890				18,032
1961	3,946		5,873				18,230
1962	4,117		6,054				18,838
1963	4,318		6,324				19,620
1964	4,622		6,887				20,472

Note: Includes Alaska and Hawaii.
SOURCE: U.S. Department of Interior.

Figure 5-10, made from the same original data as Fig. 5-9, shows how different the bands appear when the widest band is plotted first. It also depicts how any irregularity in the first band distorts those above it. Here the 1957 peak in "Mineral Fuels" reflects this rise in the other trends.

3. *The table used for plotting only.* After the arrangement of the bands has been determined, the data should be compiled for the drafting room in a special table. The amounts on this table should be added in proper sequence for plotting. Such a table should be labeled "for plotting only." Compare Tables 5-1B and 5-1C for plotting Figs. 5-9 and 5-10, respectively.

The first column of figures represents the first band. The amount of the second band added to the first band should be listed in the second column, and so on. The final figures in the last column represent the total amounts to be plotted.

In Table 5-1B, it was not necessary to fill in data for "Mineral Fuels," as the sum would equal "Total Minerals." The same is true for "Nonmetals" in Table 5-1C.

This special table requires each figure to be plotted from the *zero* line. This method has been found to be more accurate than plotting from one band to the next by means of a plotting scale. Widths of pencil marks and sliding the scale can throw accurate plotting off as points are cumulated.

4. *Labeling and shading bands.* Label the bands directly on their surface when possible. If the band is too narrow, it may be necessary to carry a legend. The total trend line which makes a silhouette of the chart should be labeled "Total" (see Fig. 5-10).

As a rule in shading surface charts, tone the first band to be the darkest and have the lightest pattern at the top. Keep diagonals of patterns in the same general direction. If, however, one band is of special interest, make that one in the darkest shading or in the most distinctive pattern.

Choose patterns carefully, for while they may be different in design, when reduced or seen at a distance they may take on similar tonal values and not have the contrast desired.

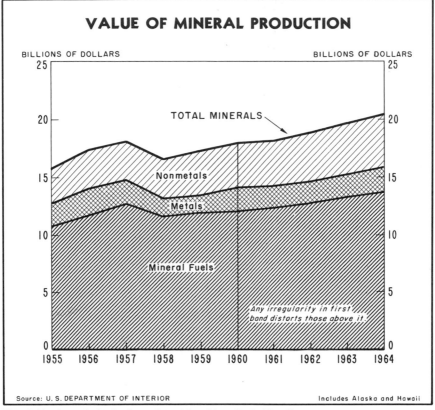

VALUE OF MINERAL PRODUCTION

FIG. 5-10   **Irregularity in first plotted band is reflected in others.**

TABLE 5-1C   *Value of Mineral Production (Millions of Dollars)*
Table 5-1A cumulated for plotting Fig. 5-10

Year	Mineral fuels	+	Metals	+	Nonmetals	=	Total minerals
1955	10,780		12,835				15,911
1956	11,741		14,099				17,490
1957	12,709		14,846				18,233
1958	11,589		13,183				16,649
1959	11,950		13,520				17,381
1960	12,142		14,164				18,032
1961	12,357		14,284				18,230
1962	12,784		14,721				18,838
1963	13,296		15,302				19,620
1964	13,585		15,850				20,472

Note: Includes Alaska and Hawaii.
SOURCE: U.S. Department of Interior.

THE 100 PERCENT SURFACE CHART

These same principles of plotting and shading should be followed for the 100 percent surface chart (see Fig. 5-11). The smoothness in trends should decide the order of plotting the bands, and the shading patterns should be chosen for tonal contrast. Above all, keep in mind that the fewer the bands or strata, the more easily the overall story may be read.

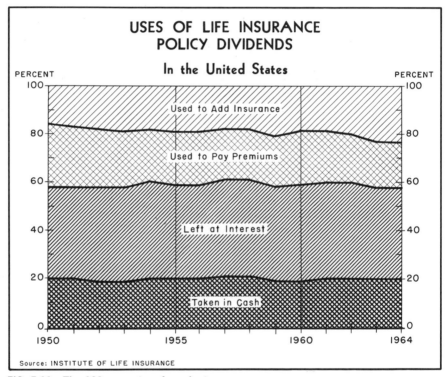

FIG. 5-11   The 100 percent surface chart.

COMBINING TYPES OF DATA

Figure 5-12 combines ten-year averages with annual plottings. Drafting the averages as columns calls attention to the fact that the data are for different periods. The columns and surface trend visually make a balanced chart.

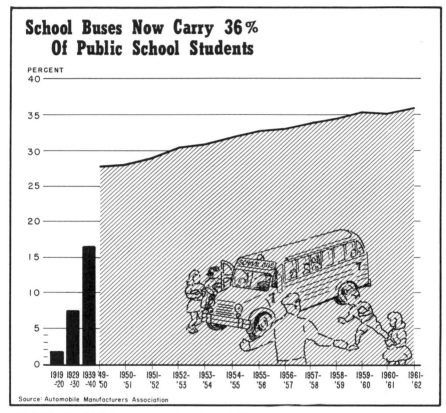

FIG. 5-12   Combining columns and surface plottings.

THE SHADED-ZONE CHART

Differences between two trends may be stressed by shading the area or *zone* between them. The chart in Fig. 5-13 accents the increase of truck and bus registrations in countries outside the United States by shading the 1950s to 1960s.

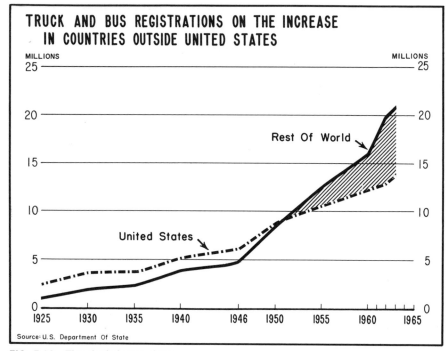

FIG. 5-13   The shaded-zone chart.

The shading in the chart in Fig. 5-14 gives a silhouette of the differences between the assessed valuation and bonded debt in Washington County, Maryland.

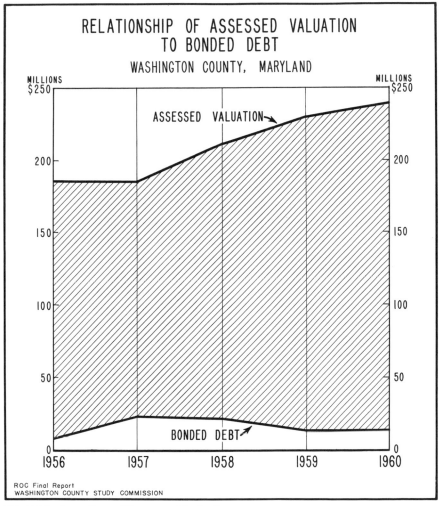

FIG. 5-14 Accenting a difference with shading.

The New York City weather chart (see Fig. 5-15) shows the highest and lowest temperatures from the city's 95-year-old record. The shaded band or zone represents the normal high and low for that city.

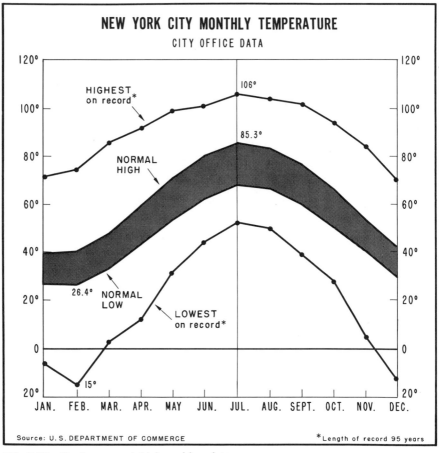

FIG. 5-15 Shading normal, high, and low data.

Figure 5-16 is a World War I presentation made by the United States Food Administration during that war. It shows top and bottom market prices of cattle at Chicago and the percent sold within the three shaded price belts. The Administration had a series of such charts.

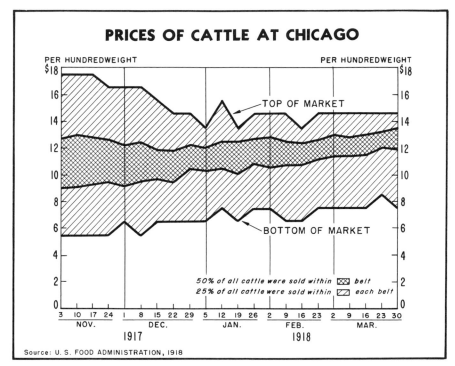

FIG. 5-16   Shading price belts.

When plotting two trends on a regular amount scale where differences in the trends are to be stressed, use two distinctive patterns of shading to show these differences.

Chart *A* in Fig. 5-17 depicts the surplus and deficit in the United States federal budget. Do not make a surface chart of these data. Chart *B* in Fig. 5-17 overemphasizes government receipts by shading that surface. The stress should be on deficit and surplus, not on receipts.

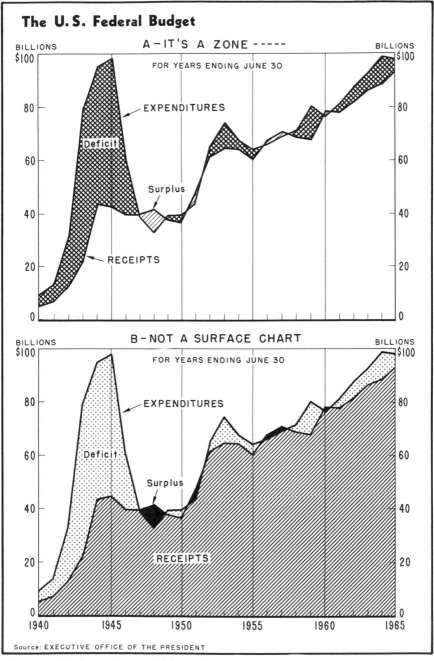

FIG. 5-17   Shading surface and deficit differences.

THE DEVIATION CHART

In the deviation-trend chart, that is, one showing positive and negative plottings, the zero line is the base line and is always drawn heavier than the other horizontal grids. The data are plotted in quadrants I and IV (see Fig. 4-1). Amounts or percentages may be shaded above or below this base line. In Fig. 5-18, only the negative percent is shaded in order to stress it.

The deviation chart is also a familiar format for the business activity charts where the base line is labeled "Normal" and the movements of the trend are above or below this line. Two shadings may be used for positive and negative plottings to make a silhouette of the trend.

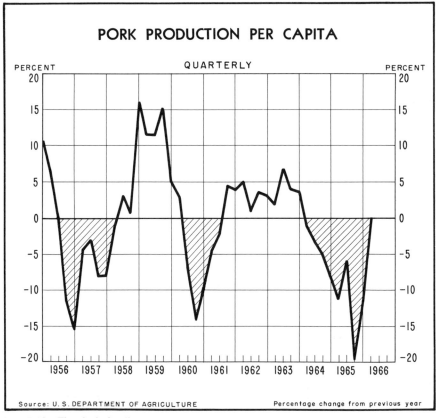

FIG. 5-18 The deviation-line chart.

SIX

Column Charts

The column chart is simple and easily read, and it appears less statistical than the standard line chart to persons not too statistically minded. At a public exhibit where charts were predominant in the displays, it was observed that the column and bar charts were noted more than other statistical types.

THE SIMPLE COLUMN CHART

The column or vertical bar chart's primary purpose is to depict numerical values of a given item over a period of time (see Table 6-1). These values are represented by the height of the columns. This type of chart accents the individual dates of the plottings rather than the trend as shown by the curve chart (see Fig. 6-1).

Particular care should be taken in the layout of a column chart when considering the width and spacing of the columns. They should all be the same width and begin at zero. As a rule, the spacing between the columns is one-half the width of the columns. If the chart is enclosed in a frame grid, one-half of this width is at the beginning and end of the chart.

163

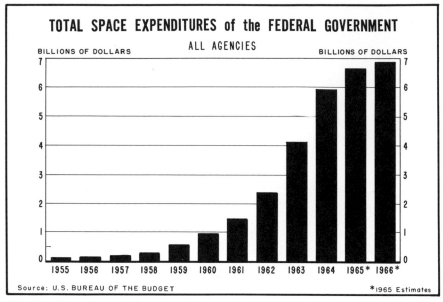

FIG. 6-1 The column chart.

TABLE 6-1 *Total Space Program Expenditures of the Federal Government (Millions of Dollars)*

Year	Expenditures	Year	Expenditures
1955	75	1961	1,468
1956	100	1962	2,387
1957	150	1963	4,079
1958	249	1964	5,930
1959	521	1965°	6,657
1960	960	1966°	6,890

° 1965 estimates.
Note: Years ending June 30.
SOURCE: U.S. Bureau of the Budget.

LAYOUT OF COLUMNS

Figure 6-2 is the pencil layout of Fig. 6-1. It shows the use of the decimal scale or ruler for spacing the amount grid and columns. While layouts can be figured mathematically, the decimal or engineer's scale will be found to be indispensable. Such a scale is divided into 10, 20, 30, 40, 50, and 60 graduations to an inch. By placing one of the decimal scales diagonally from grid to grid, the measured space can be divided accurately into the number of units needed.

In Fig. 6-2, the original amount grid was 4.2 in. high. This was to be divided into seven parts, a simple matter in this case where a 10-to-the-inch scale was used. Every 0.6 of an inch was equal to 1 billion dollars.

In dividing 7.4 in., the time scale, the draftsman was required to find the width of 12 columns, 11 spaces between columns, and half spaces before the first column and after the last column. The 40-to-an-inch scale was considered the easiest to use. By slanting this scale diagonally from zero to unit 36 between the two vertical grids, a balanced layout was marked off.

36 units on a 40 scale = 7.4 in. (width of space to be divided)
12 columns, two units wide   = 24 units
11 spaces (between columns), one unit wide   = 11 units
 2 half spaces (at beginning and end of grid) = 1 unit
                                 Total = 36 units

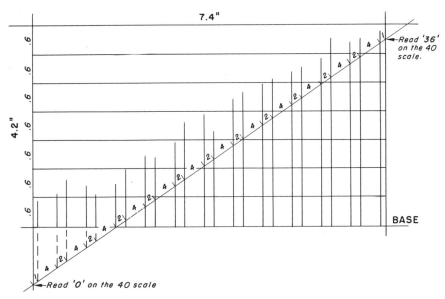

FIG. 6-2 Using the decimal rule for spacing.

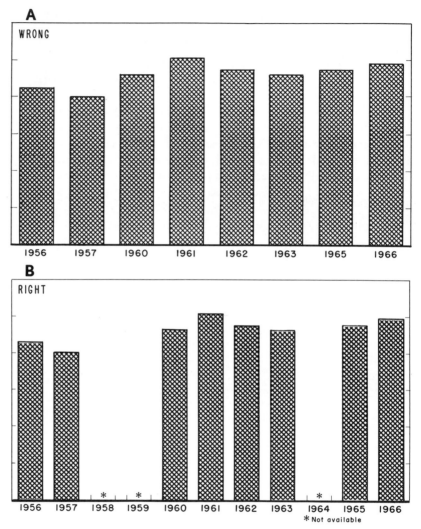

FIG. 6-3 Wrong and right spacing for missing data.

GRID FOR COLUMNS

It is not necessary to draw a full amount-scale grid for a column chart. Ticks indicating the amount scale may be adequate. When inking the grid and base line, make them a little heavier than on a line chart to make allowance for the more solid appearance of the columns.

IRREGULAR TIME SEQUENCE

If a few irregularities occur in the time sequence, spaces should be included on the time scale for the width of the missing columns. Figure 6-3A shows how easily these could be overlooked. Part B shows the correct layout.

However, a few selected dates of irregular incidence may be evenly spaced when dates are lettered clearly below each column. A subtitle should be added to denote that the data are for *selected* dates. In Fig. 6-4 the shading change further calls attention to the irregularity of the sequence. Grid is not needed on this chart, as the actual amounts are lettered inside the columns. The numerals lettered there do not interfere with a clear comparison of the heights of the columns.

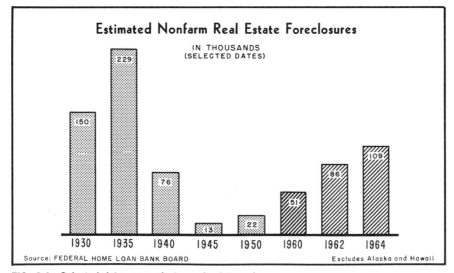

FIG. 6-4   Selected dates spaced at regular intervals.

BREAKING THE AMOUNT SCALE

As a rule the amount scale should *not* be broken in column or bar charts when an integral series of data is to be compared. If, however, there is one erratic point in the general trend that is not significant for the purpose of the chart, this column may be broken at the *top*, and the amount shown directly above it.

Chart *A* in Fig. 6-5 shows the plotting of an irregular amount on a covering scale. Assuming that this particular column is of minor interest, chart *B* shows how cutting the scale gives a better comparison of the lower amounts in the series.

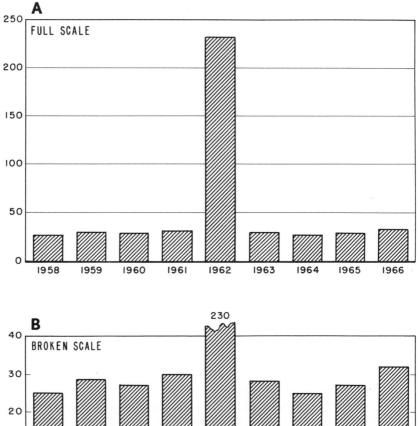

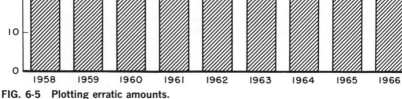

FIG. 6-5 Plotting erratic amounts.

GROUPED COLUMNS

The grouped-column chart is used to compare two or three independent series over a period of time. Too many categories in a group become difficult to follow (see Fig. 6-6).

Frequency distributions may also be portrayed with columns by grouping the categories in continuous class intervals.

Each group of columns should be separated by a space wide enough to discern easily the time period or class interval.

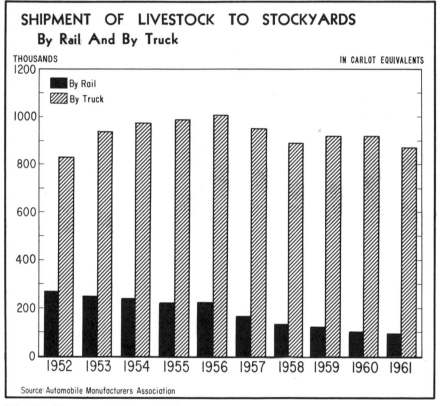

FIG. 6-6   The grouped-column chart.

Shading patterns or colors of good contrast will distinguish the columns in the groups and show effectively their difference in amounts. A legend is necessary to identify each category. This is usually in the upper left corner of the grid, but balanced layout may require that it appear as a subtitle or at the bottom of the chart.

Multiple-amount scales are to be avoided on a grouped-column chart because of the confusion of linking the key with its corresponding scale and column. When two categories are to be plotted and two scales are necessary, a paired-bar chart is suggested (see Fig. 7-19).

CONNECTED COLUMNS

The connected-column chart shows effectively the overall picture for a long period of time (see Fig. 6-7). It accents the time incidents more sharply than a line chart. This type of graph may be necessary when spaced columns would appear crowded in a time series. It is not to be confused with the histogram (see Fig. 4-30).

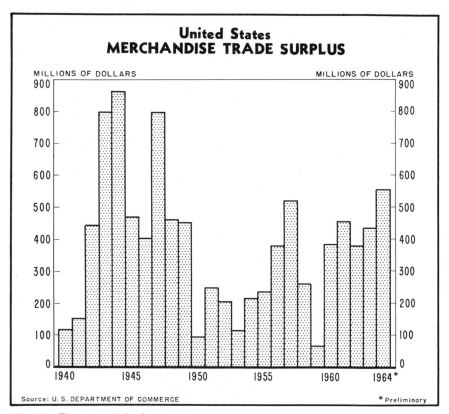

FIG. 6-7   The connected-column chart.

SUBDIVIDED COLUMNS

The subdivided-column chart shows the component parts of a total (see Fig. 6-8). While similar in purpose to the subdivided-surface chart (see Fig. 5-7) in that it shows an overall picture of the data, its other function is to define the fluctuations of the segments more sharply.

These components should be few in number, and each should carry a distinctive shading pattern. The patterns must be such that no optical illusions occur (see shading patterns in Fig. 2-18).

Usually a key or legend is necessary on a subdivided-column chart. However, since the chart in Fig. 6-8 has only two components and is fairly simple, the customary key is not necessary. The labels on the plotted surface can be easily identified.

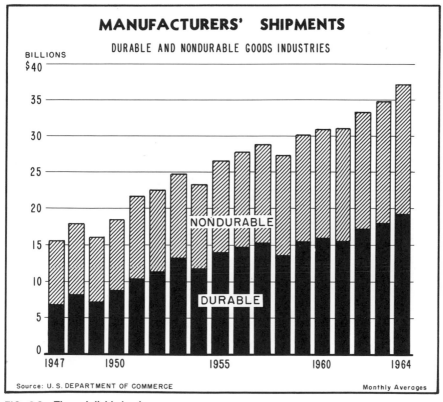

FIG. 6-8   The subdivided column.

TABLE FOR PLOTTING SUBDIVIDED-COLUMN CHARTS

The charts in Fig. 6-9 illustrate the difference between the layout and appearance of the data when plotted as a line chart and as a subdivided-column chart. While the line chart may be plotted directly from the original table, it is best for the sake of accuracy to cumulate a special table for the plotting of the subdivided-column chart (see Tables 6-2 and 6-3).

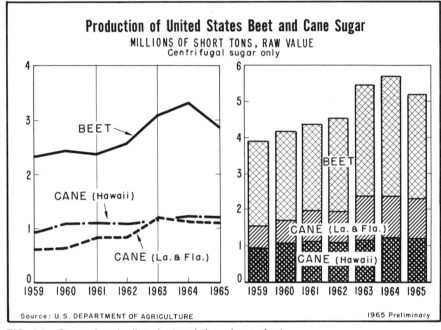

Production of United States Beet and Cane Sugar
MILLIONS OF SHORT TONS, RAW VALUE
Centrifugal sugar only

Source: U.S. DEPARTMENT OF AGRICULTURE

1965 Preliminary

FIG. 6-9   Comparing the line chart and the column chart.

TABLE 6-2   *Production of United States Beet and Cane Sugar (Thousands of Short Tons, Raw Value)*

Year	Beet	Cane (La. and Fla.)	Cane (Hawaii)	Total
1959	2,340	616	936	3,892
1960	2,450	630	1,090	4,170
1961	2,404	858	1,120	4,382
1962	2,598	853	1,101	4,552
1963	3,100	1,185	1,179	5,464
1964	3,332	1,147	1,218	5,697
1965°	2,880	1,100	1,200	5,180

° Preliminary.
Note: Covers centrifugal sugar only.
SOURCE: U.S. Department of Agriculture.

TABLE 6-3   *Production of United States Beet and Cane Sugar (Thousands of Short Tons, Raw Value)*
Table 6-2 cumulated for plotting columns in Fig. 6-9

Year	Cane (Hawaii)	+	Cane (La. and Fla.)	+ Beet =	Total
1959	936		1,552		3,892
1960	1,090		1,720		4,170
1961	1,120		1,978		4,382
1962	1,101		1,954		4,552
1963	1,179		2,364		5,464
1964	1,218		2,365		5,697
1965°	1,200		2,300		5,180

° Preliminary.

The columns in Fig. 6-10, showing population growth in Washington County, Maryland, take on a posterlike look in their layout. The trend of growth is suggested by the dashed lines connecting the columns. The component labels directly beside each component leave no doubt about the identity of the segments.

One advantage that the component column has over the subdivided-surface chart is that the actual data can be put in the shaded segments of the columns. This does away with the need of a scale. If there is not enough space to identify the shaded segments, as in Fig. 6-10, a legend must be carried on the chart (see Fig. 6-12).

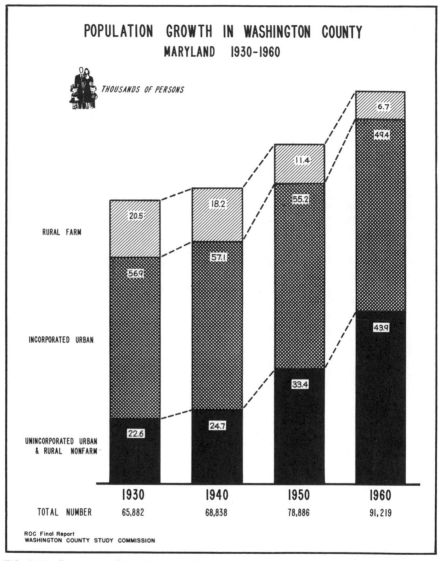

FIG. 6-10   Poster-type layout for subdivided columns.

Figure 6-11 is for an audience interested in business. It compares number of establishments and sales in wholesale trade for two periods. Here again there is no doubt about the labeling of segments and the amounts of each shading.

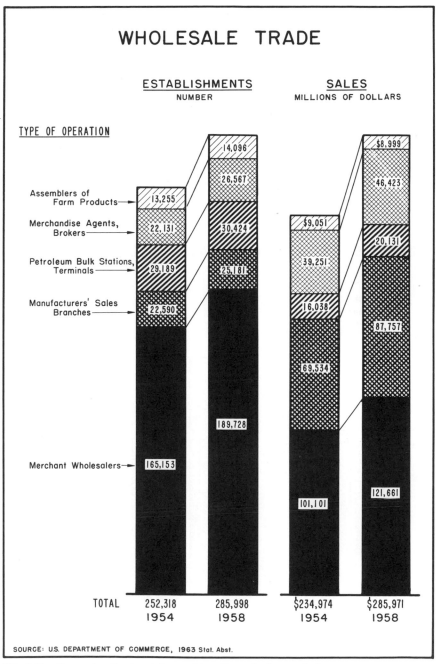

WHOLESALE TRADE

ESTABLISHMENTS
NUMBER

SALES
MILLIONS OF DOLLARS

TYPE OF OPERATION

Assemblers of
Farm Products— 13,255

Merchandise Agents,
Brokers— 22,131

Petroleum Bulk Stations,
Terminals— 29,189

Manufacturers' Sales
Branches— 22,590

14,096

26,567

30,424

25,181

189,728

$8,999

46,423

20,131

87,757

$9,051

39,251

16,038

69,534

Merchant Wholesalers— 165,153

121,661

101,101

TOTAL   252,318   285,998 $234,974 $285,971
          1954   1958   1954   1958

SOURCE: U.S. DEPARTMENT OF COMMERCE, 1963 Stat. Abst.

FIG. 6-11   Comparing the breakdown of two items for two periods.

THE THREE-DIMENSIONAL COLUMN

The three-dimensional chart, drawn by perspective projection, is not highly recommended (see Fig. 2-22). It may seem to be dressy and attract attention, but that is about all it does.

It is much easier to estimate the amounts of the components in the chart in Fig. 6-12, as the vertical and horizontal scales are drawn at right angles. However, the total amounts of the columns appear larger because of the third dimension, and the shading on the sides of the columns introduces another concept. It is bad charting to try to tell too much on one chart. Anything that must be studied for its meaning is not good for popular presentation.

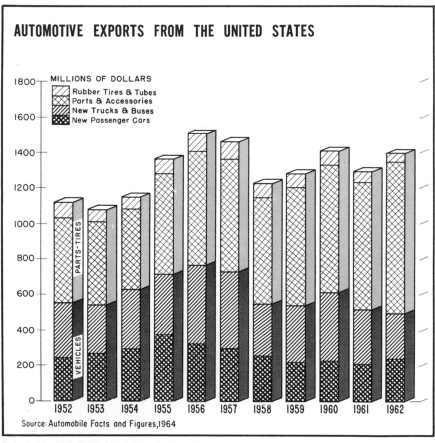

FIG. 6-12   Subdivided columns in the third dimension.

THE 100 PERCENT COLUMN

There are two amount aspects to read in Fig. 6-13. The columns are plotted in *cents* and represent the cost of a pound loaf of bread to the consumer. The numerals in the shaded segments are *percentages* showing the relative proportion of the total cost to the consumer added at each stage of handling. The sum of the percentages in each column equals 100 percent. This is one of the United States Food Administration charts made in 1918. Note that the change of time in the horizontal scale has been clearly indicated.

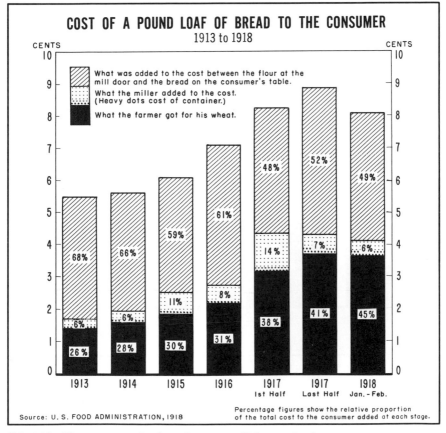

FIG. 6-13   When an amount column becomes a 100 percent column.

The components of the 100 percent column chart show their relationship to the whole column (see Fig. 6-14). If there is a choice of which segment should be plotted first, the one of most interest has that place, as it can easily be read from the base line. A cumulated table should be made for plotting the segments similar to Table 6-3.

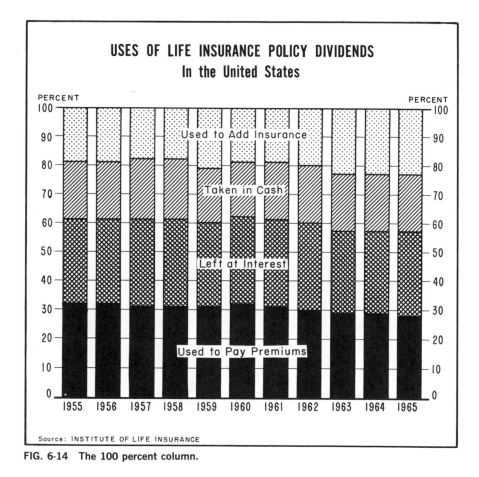

FIG. 6-14 The 100 percent column.

Figure 6-15, unlike the time series plotting in Fig. 6-14, compares by civil defense regions how long food on hand could be made to last. The segments are plotted progressively by the length of time the food was estimated to hold out. The regions are identified in the small map.

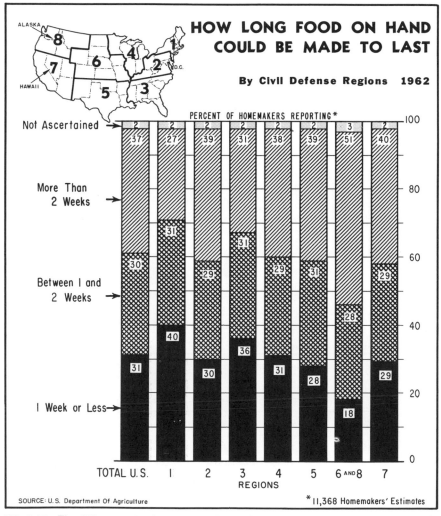

FIG. 6-15   The 100 percent column comparing regions.

THE DEVIATION COLUMN

The deviation column provides a method for plotting increases and decreases, losses and gains, or deviation from a requirement or norm. The chart in Fig. 6-16 shows the change in dollars in business inventories from year to year. Leave an even space between each column. Data are in Table 6-4.

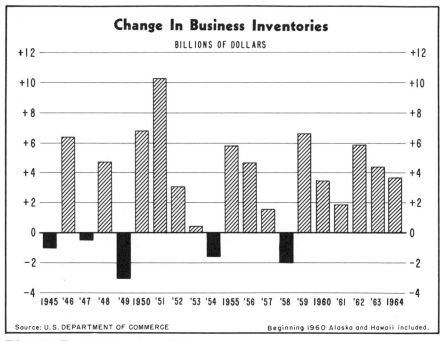

FIG. 6-16   The deviation-column chart.

TABLE 6-4   *Changes in Business Inventories (Billions of Dollars)*

Year	Inventory	Year	Inventory	Year	Inventory
1945	−1.1	1952	3.1	1959	6.6
1946	6.4	1953	0.4	1960	3.5
1947	−0.5	1954	−1.6	1961	1.9
1948	4.7	1955	5.8	1962	5.9
1949	−3.1	1956	4.7	1963	4.4
1950	6.8	1957	1.6	1964	3.7
1951	10.2	1958	−2.0		

SOURCE: U.S. Department of Commerce, 1965.

In the deviation chart, each column is either positive or negative, never both. The columns representing either percents or absolute numbers are plotted above the base line for positive amounts and below the base line for negative amounts. The grouped-column chart in Fig. 6-17 shows the differences from the preceding year. The groups are separated by a white space.

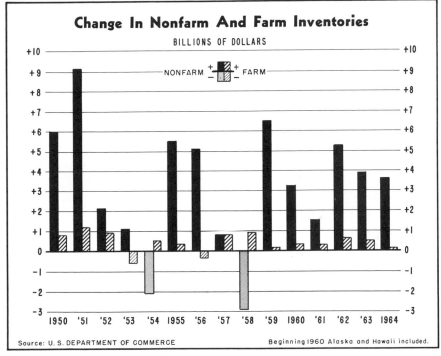

FIG. 6-17   Grouped deviation columns.

THE HIGH-LOW CHART

The high-low chart permits the plotting of the range of maximal and minimal values for a time series. The top of the column represents the high value, and the bottom the low. At times a line or symbol of some type is shown on the column indicating an average or some specific comparative point.

High-low plottings may be amounts or percentages for weeks, months, etc., or quotations as of selected dates. Figure 6-18 shows the high and low index of prices received by farmers for feed grains from 1951 to 1964. The dashed line represents the average price index for each year.

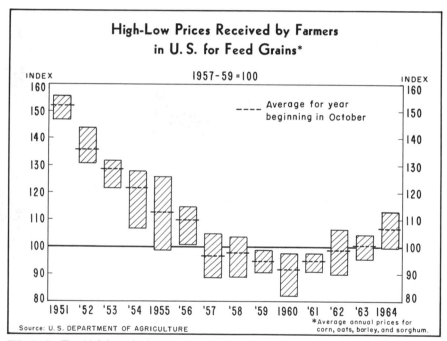

FIG. 6-18   The high-low chart.

The format of this chart appears frequently in weather reports showing high and low temperatures of the day and month. It is also seen in the familiar stock-market reports showing the high and low points in stock transactions of the day. In the case of stock-market reports a symbol often indicates the opening and closing points for the day.

Figure 6-19 not only depicts the high and low *number* of factory sales of passenger cars in the United States for each year, but indicates, in the accompanying score chart, the high and low *months* in which the sales were made.

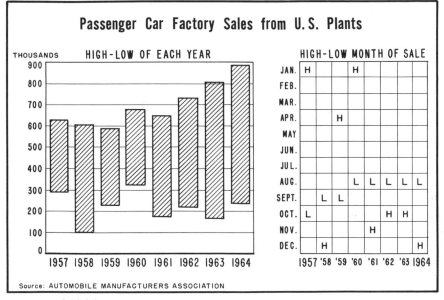

FIG. 6-19 A high-low score.

THE FLOATING COLUMN

The floating column is a subdivided-column chart in which two components make up the *total height* of the column, representing a total amount or 100 percent.

One component is plotted above the base line, the other directly below it. Unlike the deviation-column chart in Fig. 6-16, both plottings are positive.

In the chart in Fig. 6-20, the total length of the column represents the gross revenue of television broadcasting. The amount above the zero line is the net revenue, and that below the base represents expenses. The number of stations involved each year is in italics at the bottom of the chart.

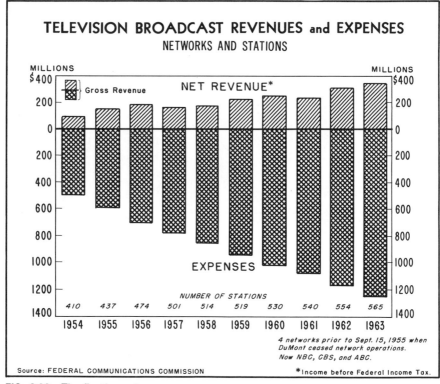

FIG. 6-20   The floating column.

COMBINING TYPES OF CHARTS

One can stress a particular message or elaborate on a story by combining different types of charts, such as a trend-curve or a shaded-surface chart with a column chart, or a pie chart with either a curve or column chart (see Figs. 5-12, 8-4, and 8-5).

COLUMNS AND TRENDS

The columns and curves plotted in Fig. 6-21 compare the trend of automotive color popularity for three selected years. The colors are arranged by the 1965 preference.

Columns were used for the latest year, 1965, in order that that year would stand out. Color categories are lettered at an angle to facilitate the reading of their names.

WORK-LOAD RECORD

Figure 6-22 gives a broad picture of the work at hand. The first chart portrays, by means of a subdivided-surface chart, the number of contracts coming in during the month and those on hand from the previous month. The deviation-column chart shows the status of the work load, whether there was a net lag or gain; and the line chart depicts the number of contracts completed and those incomplete. This type of layout has varied uses for record keeping or storyboards.

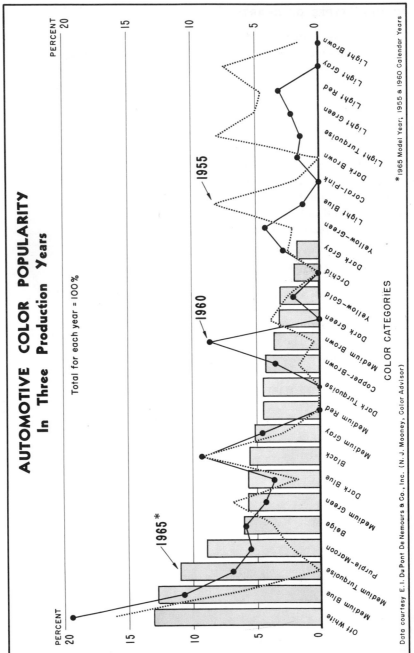

FIG. 6-21 Comparing columns with curves.

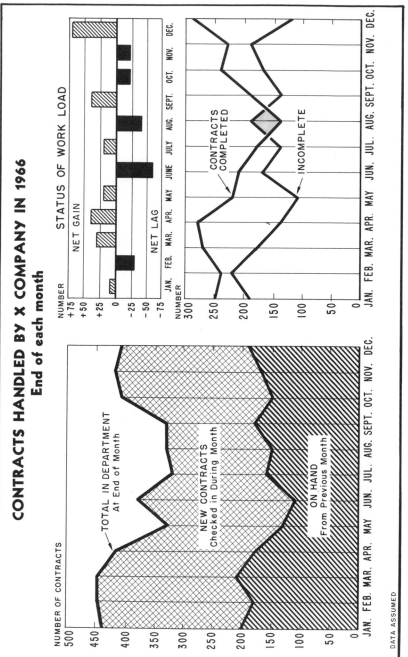

FIG. 6-22 Monthly work-load-record charts.

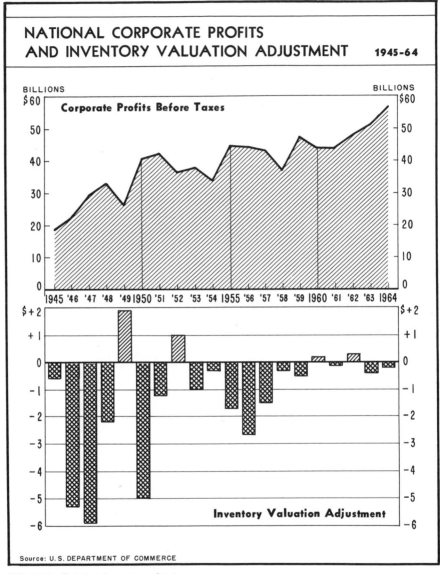

FIG. 6-23   Relative inventory charts.

PLOTTING RELATIVE CHARTS

Figure 6-23 shows a surface chart depicting corporate profits before taxes, and a deviation chart of inventory-valuation adjustment. Both charts are closely associated by means of a common time period. It is essential that such a layout be accurately drawn, so that the plottings on both charts correspond to the exact periods of time.

The diagram in Fig. 6-24 shows how to divide a given space to accommodate both trend and column plottings. First, lay out the *areas* for the two charts. In this case it was found that, by using the 40 divisions to an inch on the engineer's scale, 20 columns could be laid out with good spacing. Detailed measurements are lettered on the diagram. See Fig. 6-23 for finished layout.

The grid for plotting the surface trend should be placed directly over the *midpoint* width of the column.

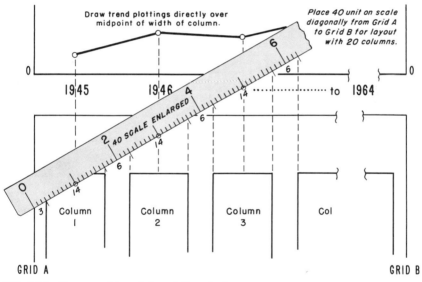

FIG. 6-24   Diagram of layout for relative charts.

SEVEN

The Bar Chart

The horizontal-bar chart compares effectively *different items as of a specified time* (see Table 7-1). The bars originate at the right from a common base line. Their lengths are measured by a horizontal scale. Never omit the *zero* when labeling the scale.

TABLE 7-1 *Leading Television Adver-tisers, 1965, Net Time and Program Costs (Millions of Dollars)*

Advertiser	Cost
Toiletries and toilet goods	$265
Food and food products	205
Smoking materials	145
Drugs and remedies	144
Soaps, cleansers, and polishes	112

SOURCE: Television Bureau of Advertising, Inc., New York.

The vertical axis lists the various items to be compared. In the simple bar chart in Fig. 7-1, the horizontal scale measures the millions of dollars spent, while the vertical dimension lists the leading television advertisers.

Distinguish horizontal-*bar* charts from the vertical-*column* charts, as they are two different types of presentations, each having its own specified use.

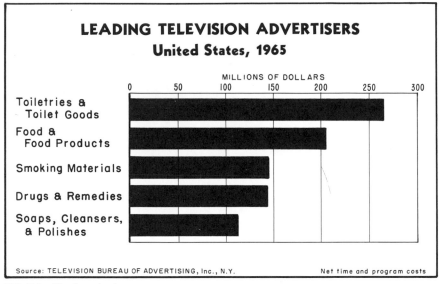

LEADING TELEVISION ADVERTISERS
United States, 1965

MILLIONS OF DOLLARS

Source: TELEVISION BUREAU OF ADVERTISING, Inc., N.Y.   Net time and program costs

FIG. 7-1   The bar chart.

PLANNING THE LAYOUT

Spacing and width of bars in the layout should be carefully considered from the visual point of view. All bars are made the *same* width, and the space between them, as a rule, should be one-half the width of a bar. This spacing will be narrower when many items are to be plotted. Do not make it wider than the width of the bar, as it tends to visually weaken the appearance of the chart.

When dividing the grid laid out for the chart into bars and spaces between them, use the same method as for column-chart layouts. (See Fig. 6-2, adapting it to the bar format.)

LABELING BARS

The labeling of bars depends very much on the size of the layout and the use of the charts. Ordinarily the stub, that is, the list of items, is lettered to the left of each bar, while the amount scale denotes the magnitude of the items.

However, when the width and length of the bar permits it, the actual data should be lettered in the bars to give a quicker conception of the magnitude. The bars lettered in this manner are particularly suitable for displays or for visuals used at conferences where charts may be closely examined (see Fig. 7-2).

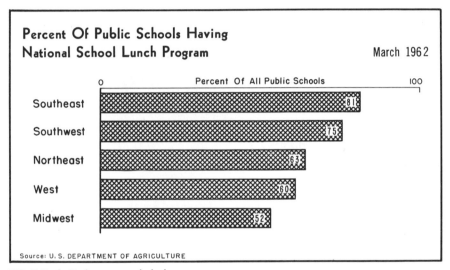

FIG. 7-2   Lettering numerals in bars.

While ample room should be provided for legibility, lettering should not dominate the picture, as the bars are the major interest. Various methods of labeling are shown in Fig. 7-3.

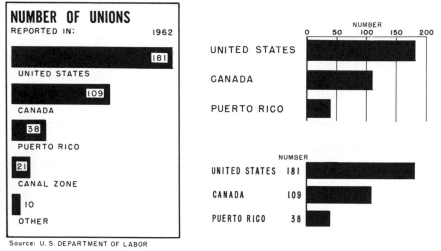

FIG. 7-3   Labeling the bar chart.

SEQUENCE OF ITEMS

The sequence of items represented by the bars depends upon the purpose of the chart and the nature of the given data. This sequence may be arranged in numerical (quantitative), alphabetical, progressive, qualitative, chronological, or geographic order.

1. Numerical order. When the chart is to show the order of the data in magnitude, the bars should be arranged numerically. They may be in descending or ascending order. In Fig. 7-4, it can clearly be seen which states are above or below the dashed line representing the United States average.

2. Alphabetical order. In an alphabetical arrangement, the lengths of the bars appear irregularly aligned, but the categories or, in the case of the chart in Fig. 7-5, the states may be more readily singled out.

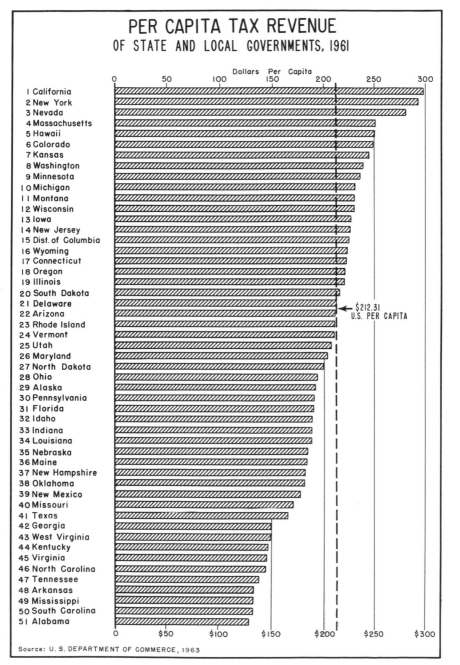

PER CAPITA TAX REVENUE
OF STATE AND LOCAL GOVERNMENTS, 1961

Dollars Per Capita

1	California
2	New York
3	Nevada
4	Massachusetts
5	Hawaii
6	Colorado
7	Kansas
8	Washington
9	Minnesota
10	Michigan
11	Montana
12	Wisconsin
13	Iowa
14	New Jersey
15	Dist. of Columbia
16	Wyoming
17	Connecticut
18	Oregon
19	Illinois
20	South Dakota
21	Delaware
22	Arizona
23	Rhode Island
24	Vermont
25	Utah
26	Maryland
27	North Dakota
28	Ohio
29	Alaska
30	Pennsylvania
31	Florida
32	Idaho
33	Indiana
34	Louisiana
35	Nebraska
36	Maine
37	New Hampshire
38	Oklahoma
39	New Mexico
40	Missouri
41	Texas
42	Georgia
43	West Virginia
44	Kentucky
45	Virginia
46	North Carolina
47	Tennessee
48	Arkansas
49	Mississippi
50	South Carolina
51	Alabama

← $212.31
U.S. PER CAPITA

Source: U. S. DEPARTMENT OF COMMERCE, 1963

FIG. 7-4   Bars numerically arranged.

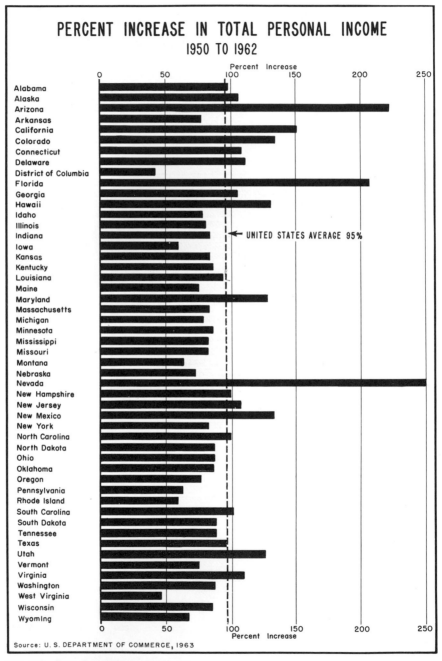

FIG. 7-5   Bars alphabetically arranged.

3. *Progressive order.* The bar chart may be used to advantage for showing progress of some particular project or schedule of work. Departments, sections, types of jobs, or similar subjects are listed to the left of the base line; while the amount scale, denoting hours, days, weeks, etc., charts the work completed or achieved. This method is used in matériel-control charts, Gantt charts (see Figs. 8-15 and 8-16), quota charts, or charts where status of progress is shown. Figure 7-6 is a quota chart used in a community Red Cross drive.

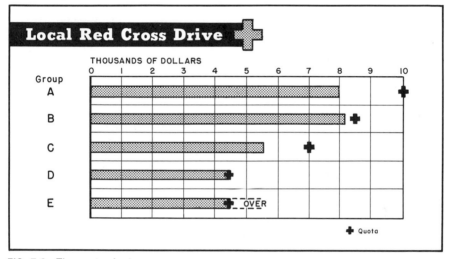

FIG. 7-6   The quota chart.

4. *Qualitative order.* When some quality or attribute essential
to the data is listed, bars are particularly appropriate (see Fig. 7-7).
The qualifying attributes are listed to the left of the bars, and the
length of the bars designates the amount. This arrangement is for
data covering one period of time.

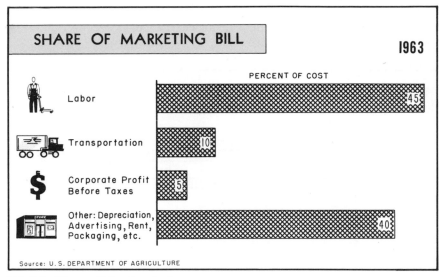

FIG. 7-7   The qualitative-bar chart.

5. *Chronological order.* The bar format may be used when the data lend themselves to a few selected dates. The figures of children are adapted to the bar layout in Fig. 7-8. This repetition of design within bars is often referred to as a *wallpaper* pictorial.

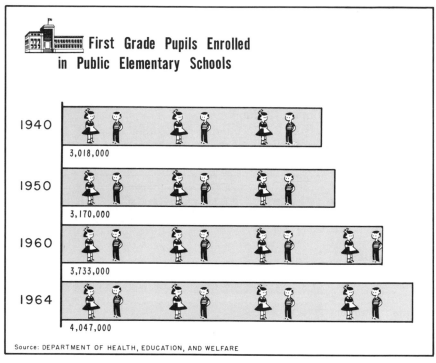

FIG. 7-8   Pictorials in bars.

6. *Geographic order.* There will be a need occasionally to plot bars in a geographic order. In the charts in Fig. 7-25, the grouped bars are arranged by regions in the United States. Other geographic divisions may be used, the order of the bars depending upon the objective of the chart.

BREAKING THE BAR

As a rule bars should not be broken, as a false conclusion could easily be derived from the graph. If, however, the total length of the longest bar is not essential to the whole picture, break it and insert the numeral in the *broken* portion. This numeral should always appear in such cases, whether or not a scale is used.

The broken bar in Fig. 7-9 is permissible, for if the full length had been plotted, the other amounts could not have been read. With the numerals shown in the bars, it can readily be estimated that the number of passenger cars imported to the United States from West Germany is about $4\frac{1}{2}$ times that of the longest complete bar, the United Kingdom.

The plotting of the imports from other countries is scaled in relation to the length of the United Kingdom bar.

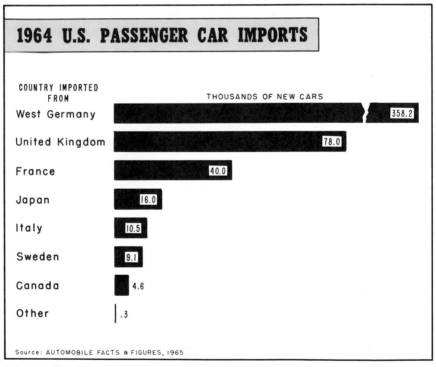

FIG. 7-9   Breaking the bar.

FOCAL POINTS

Comparing several items with a total, average, estimate, or particular focal point can be depicted in several ways. The first chart in Figure 7-10 shows the all-county average as a solid bar, while the second chart uses a dashed line and shading.

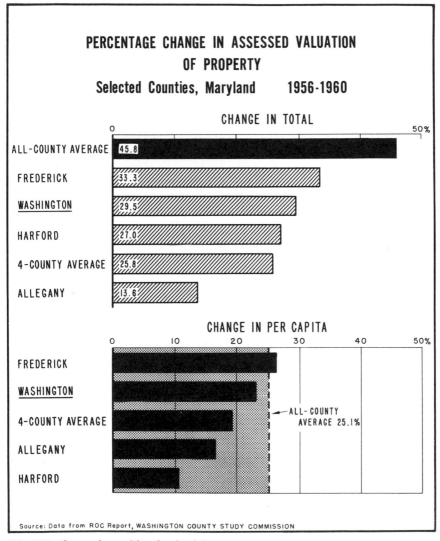

FIG. 7-10   Comparison with a focal point.

GROUPED BARS

The grouped-bar chart compares a number of items in two, or sometimes three, respects at the same time. The comparison of more than three items can become confusing.

The sequence of the groups may be numerical, alphabetical, or whatever the major category determines. The arrangement within the groups is usually a time factor, the earliest date being plotted first. Always keep the categories in the same order as was set up in the first group.

A marked contrast in shading should exist within the groups in order that the bars may be readily identified with the legend. The chart in Fig. 7-11 is arranged alphabetically to show the kinds of fruits and vegetables shipped out of California and Arizona. It compares the percent of total production shipped for the years 1954 and 1960. The latest date considered carries the darkest shading.

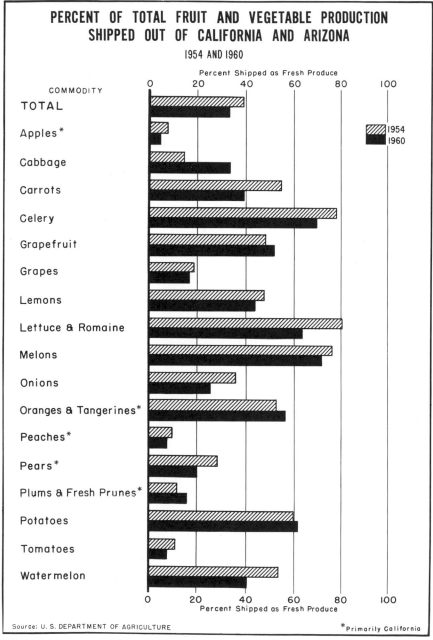

PERCENT OF TOTAL FRUIT AND VEGETABLE PRODUCTION
SHIPPED OUT OF CALIFORNIA AND ARIZONA
1954 AND 1960

Source: U. S. DEPARTMENT OF AGRICULTURE   *Primarily California

FIG. 7-11   The grouped-bar chart.

LEGENDS

A legend or key is necessary to identify categories in the grouped-bar chart; it is usually placed within the body of the chart, as in Fig. 7-12. If this position seems to interfere with the reading of the bars, place the legend under the title or subtitle, as in the component-bar chart in Fig. 7-15.

Figure 7-12 is numerically arranged by the latest time period. Data under the languages listed denote the actual number of students gained or lost in enrollment in the specified foreign language. Russian was offered in 1958, and Chinese in 1962.

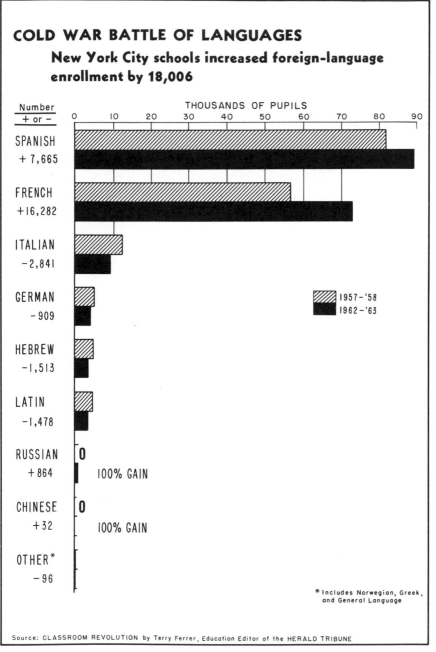

COLD WAR BATTLE OF LANGUAGES
New York City schools increased foreign-language
enrollment by 18,006

Number
+ or −

THOUSANDS OF PUPILS

0   10   20   30   40   50   60   70   80   90

SPANISH
+ 7,665

FRENCH
+16,282

ITALIAN
−2,841

GERMAN
−909

1957−'58
1962−'63

HEBREW
−1,513

LATIN
−1,478

RUSSIAN
+864

0

100% GAIN

CHINESE
+32

0

100% GAIN

OTHER*
−96

*Includes Norwegian, Greek,
and General Language

Source: CLASSROOM REVOLUTION by Terry Ferrer, Education Editor of the HERALD TRIBUNE

FIG. 7-12 Grouped bars numerically arranged.

SPACING GROUPED BARS

The space between a two-bar grouping is usually the width of one bar. However, if the area allotted is limited, the space may be made narrower, as in Fig. 7-11. The spacing between a three-bar grouping should be approximately $1\frac{1}{2}$ times the width of one bar.

THE CONNECTED-BAR CHART

The connected-bar chart, unlike the connected-column chart which extends over a period of time, may be used when a few *selected* dates are to be compared. Figure 7-13 gives a picture of the growth of the retail florist industry for four selected years. This format may also be used when comparing groups of related items.

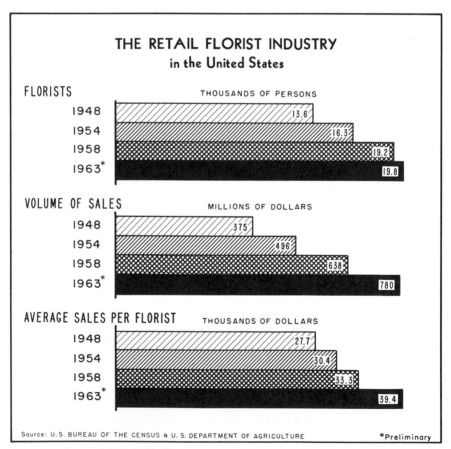

FIG. 7-13 Grouped bars in profile.

THE SUBDIVIDED-BAR CHART

The subdivided-bar or component-bar chart gives a general visual aspect of the composition of each bar. The segments, identified by a legend, should be few with shadings clearly defined. Plot the most important segment next to the base line, as in that position the value will be most easily read. The nature of the data depends upon the order in which the items are plotted.

Figure 7-14 is in numerical order with the materials purchased for insulation in standard passenger cars plotted next to the zero line.

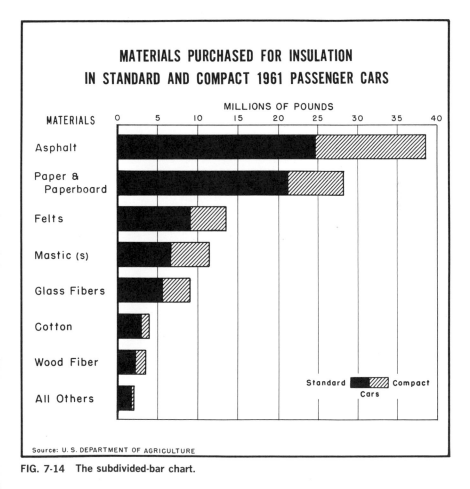

FIG. 7-14   The subdivided-bar chart.

If there are more than two components, prepare a table for plotting only, similar to the one used for plotting the subdivided-column chart (see Tables 6-2 and 6-3).

Columns are more suitable than bars for frequency-distribution charts. But in the case of Fig. 7-15, the class intervals were irregular, and the space allotted the chart was narrow, making a bar format suitable.

In this chart it is difficult to read amounts of all classes accurately, but visual comparisons of shadings give an approximate estimate of the number of accidents. It can be seen from the "Both Sexes" group that, of the known accidents, more persons are injured in the home than in the other places categorized.

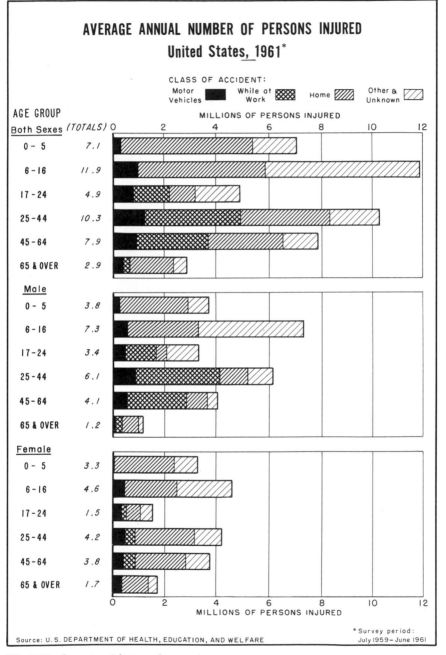

AVERAGE ANNUAL NUMBER OF PERSONS INJURED
United States, 1961*

CLASS OF ACCIDENT:
Motor Vehicles ■   While at Work ▨   Home ▨   Other & Unknown ▨

AGE GROUP
MILLIONS OF PERSONS INJURED

Source: U.S. DEPARTMENT OF HEALTH, EDUCATION, AND WELFARE

*Survey period: July 1959 – June 1961

FIG. 7-15   Component bars as frequencies.

100 PERCENT BARS

In the 100 percent bar chart the bars are of equal length and width and are divided into segments representing the percentage distribution within each category.

Figure 7-16, made from data on conditions of *total* housing in the Appalachian region, would tell another story if the Pennsylvania portion of the region were excluded. Housing conditions are relatively high in this portion. The exclusion of the Pennsylvania data from the Appalachian compilation would reduce the proportion of *sound* Appalachian housing from 73 to 67 percent; *dilapidated* housing would increase from 7.5 to 10 percent; and *deteriorating* housing would increase from 19 to 23 percent.

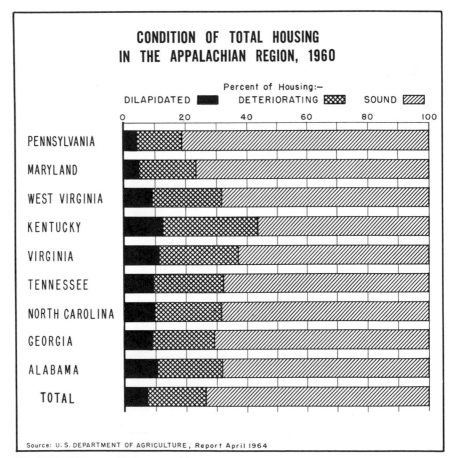

FIG. 7-16   100 percent component bar.

The 100 percent bar in Fig. 7-17 is arranged in numerical order. The legend at the bottom of the bars is not immediately noticed, although it is clearly labeled. A quicker identification is made when the legend appears nearer the title.

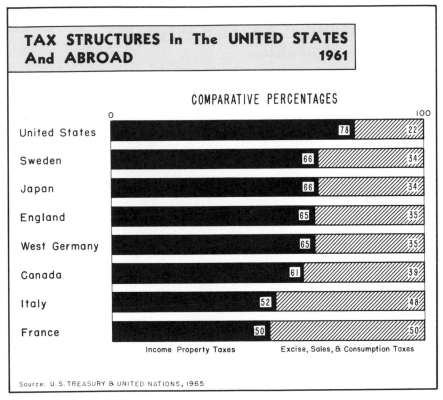

FIG. 7-17   100 percent bar numerically arranged.

The chart in Fig. 7-18 shows the 100 percent bar in a step format. It makes a simple and effective presentation when breaking a total bar into segments.

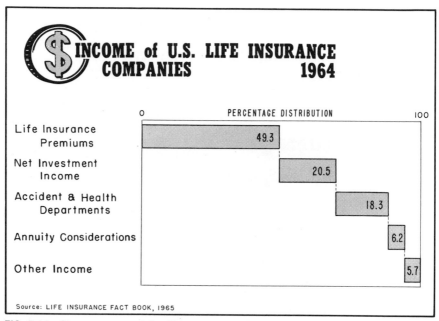

FIG. 7-18   Step arrangement for 100 percent bar chart.

PAIRED BARS

The paired-bar chart provides a method whereby *two different* horizontal scales may be used to compare a number of items in two respects (see Table 7-2).

The items are listed between the two sets of categories. One set of bars extends to the right of the listed items, the other set is directly opposite and to the left. Each set has its own scale.

The more important category is plotted to the right, as it can be read more quickly there.

In Fig. 7-19, the right category represents the amount of money given, while the left denotes the number of donors. The items listed represent those who supported the program.

Figure 7-20 compares trends in automotive color popularity for two years. Each year equals 100 percent. The breakdown by color choice was numerically arranged from the 1965 data.

TABLE 7-2   *George Washington University, 1964–1965 Annual Support Program (July 1, 1964–August 31, 1965)*

Donors	Number	Amount
Alumni		
Medicine	844	$ 47,481.96
Law	784	42,948.04
Honorary	5	16,769.73
Columbian	742	14,843.15
Engineering	292	9,767.29
Government	288	8,417.78
Education	269	3,868.00
Former students		
(inactive schools)	60	3,536.00
Graduate Council	86	1,974.00
General studies	112	1,539.50
Total alumni giving	3,482	$151,145.45
Other:		
Friends	91	44,189.03
Companies	48	40,668.82
Grand total	3,621	$236,003.30

SOURCE: *The George Washington University Newsletter,* Washington, D.C.

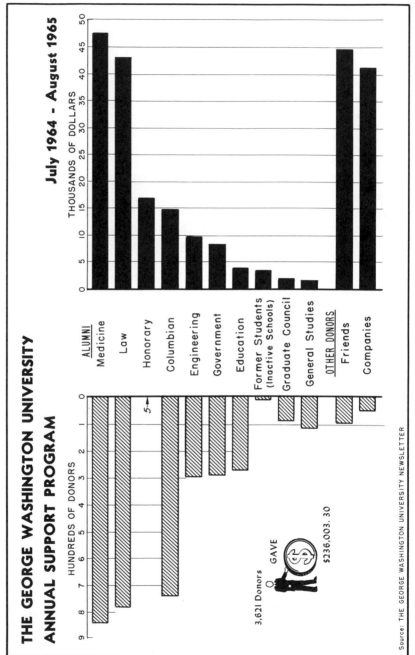

FIG. 7-19 The paired-bar chart.

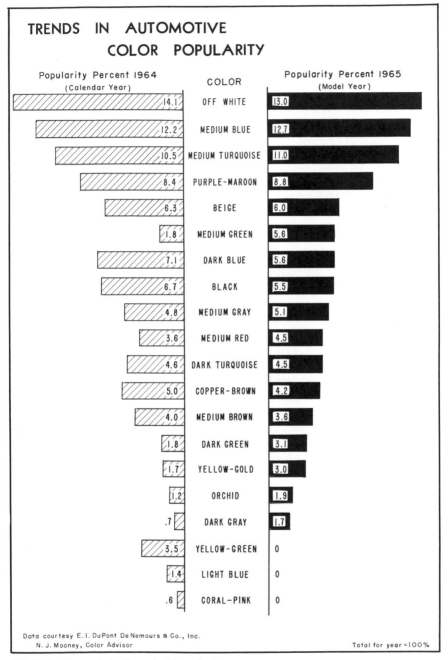

FIG. 7-20 Percents in the paired-bar chart.

Titles may be tricky. In Fig. 7-21, "The Entertainment Field" is meant to catch your eye, and it will if you are interested in that field. But you must read the body of the chart to see that it shows employment and payrolls. If employment and payrolls were included in the title or as a subtitle, one would have an immediate understanding of the purpose of the chart.

The main items are listed by their importance in the entertainment field; direct employment and annual payrolls are shown in actual amount.

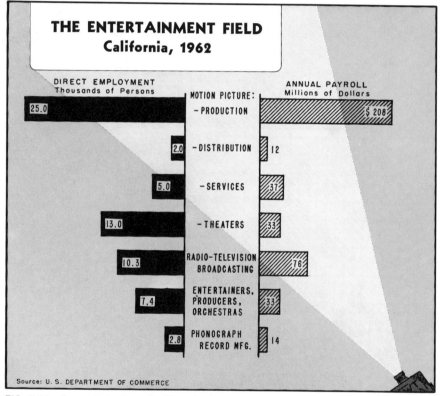

FIG. 7-21   Amounts in the paired-bar chart.

A time series may be plotted as a paired-bar chart when the nature of the data is more readable in that format.

In Fig. 7-22 the data are of two trends over a long period of time. It was desired to plot the two series independently. The paired-bar was preferred over the multiple-amount-scale line chart (see Fig. 4-12), as the profile of the bars gave a clearer and more immediate picture of the amounts.

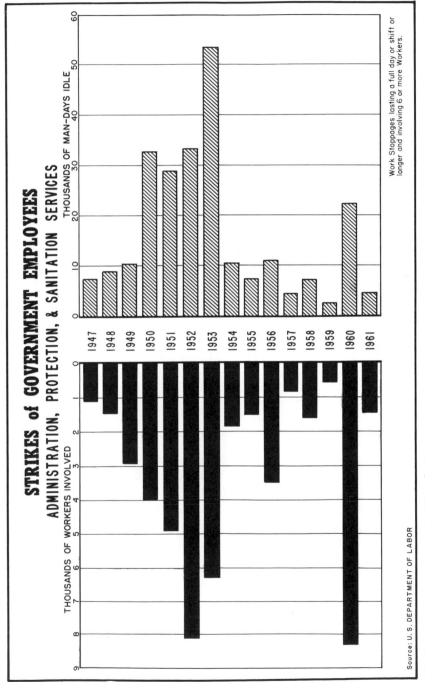

FIG. 7-22   A time series as a paired-bar chart.

BAR-AND-SYMBOL CHART

The bar-and-symbol chart may be used, instead of the grouped-bar, when comparing data by a single scale. A heavy line or various symbols may denote the supplementary data being compared to the basic bar chart.

The chart in Fig. 7-23 makes use of a heavy line symbol to show the difference between the earlier data and the later. The 1963 data are represented by a horizontal bar, and the 1954 data by a heavy vertical line. When the line extends beyond the bar, a dashed line connects the two. This type of chart condenses the presentation and yet tells the story clearly.

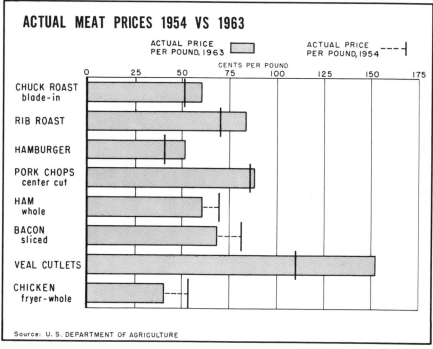

FIG. 7-23   The bar-and-symbol chart.

THE DEVIATION BAR

The deviation-bar chart presents percentage or amount changes, increase and decrease, profit and loss, or similar data by means of positive and negative scales extending to the right and left of a common base line (see Table 7-3).

If the data adapt to a numerical listing, the positive sequence, extending to the right, is arranged in descending order; the negative sequence, extending to the left of the base line, is in ascending order.

TABLE 7-3   *Industrial Life Insurance in Force in the United States, by Region*

Region	Percent change, 1954–1964
East South Central	+35.3
West South Central	+32.6
Mountain	+27.8
South Atlantic	+27.1
Pacific	−0.8
East North Central	−3.3
West North Central	−9.5
Middle Atlantic	−20.1
New England	−23.4
United States	+3.0

Note: Alaska and Hawaii are excluded from 1954 data.
SOURCE: Institute of Life Insurance.

The chart in Fig. 7-24 shows, by numerical arrangement, the percentage increase and decrease in industrial life insurance in force, by regions, in the United States.

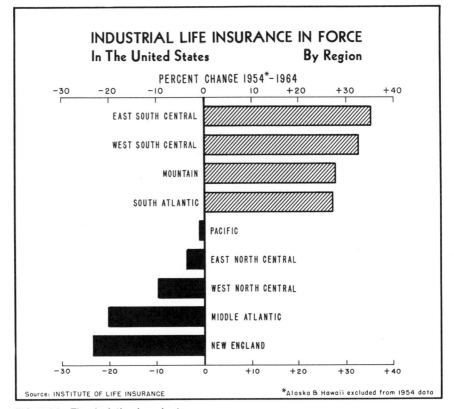

FIG. 7-24 The deviation-bar chart.

The charts in Fig. 7-25, comparing two dates in selected regions, are geographically arranged. They depict the wage changes in retail trade by cents per hour and by percent change. The West far exceeded the other regions of the United States.

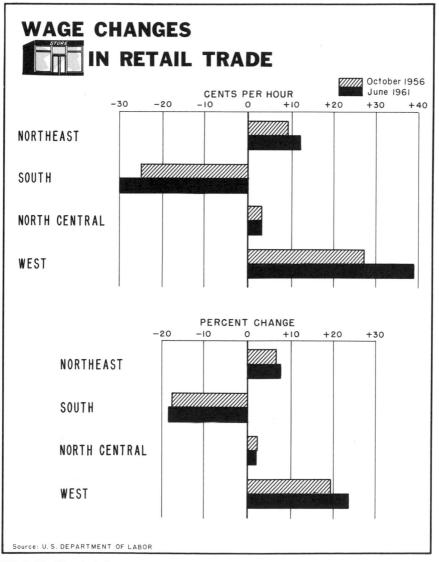

FIG. 7-25 The deviation–grouped-bar chart.

THE RANGE BAR

When high and low points of several items are to be compared, a range chart will give a simple visual comparison. The data may be wage rates, costs, values, family income, weather, etc.

The bars are not aligned at the base, but each starts at its low point and ends at its high. The horizontal scale measures the length of the bar. The result is a comparison of their ranges.

Figure 7-26 compares the horsepower of diesel engines made by several companies for industrial use.

A third value can be added to this type of chart by using a conventional symbol to represent an average or other measure.

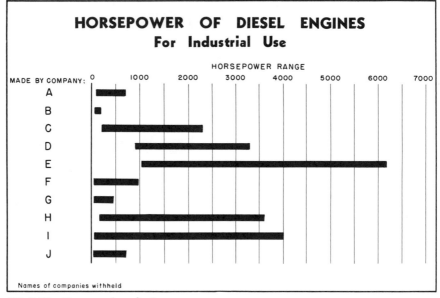

FIG. 7-26   The range-bar chart.

Figure 7-27 gives the minimum, maximum, and arithmetic average of air pollution in 17 selected cities.

Air pollution is defined as the presence in the air of substances put there by the activities of man, in concentrations sufficient to interfere with comfort, safety, or health, or with use and engagement of property. Data represent values of samples taken nationally on a biweekly basis by the National Air Sampling Network.

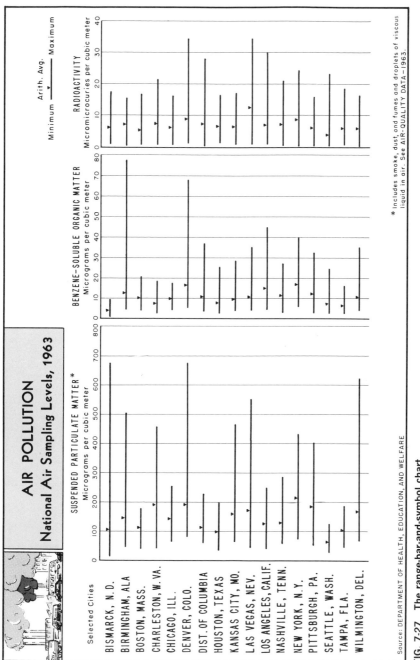

FIG. 7-27   The range-bar-and-symbol chart.

Table 7-4 lists the 17 selected cities in Fig. 7-27.

Other uses of the range bar are shown in Fig. 7-28. Part *A* shows its use as a bench mark for judging performance. Part *B* depicts how clearly an interquartile range can be indicated.

TABLE 7-4   *Air Pollution (National Air Sampling Levels, 1963)*

Selected cities	Suspended particulate matter°, micrograms per cubic meter		
	Minimum	*Maximum*	*Arithmetic avg.*
Bismark, N. Dak.	15	679	108
Birmingham, Ala.	49	505	149
Boston, Mass.	42	180	114
Charleston, W.Va.	42	459	192
Chicago, Ill.	67	257	144
Denver, Colo.	86	673	191
District of Columbia	63	231	116
Houston, Tex.	37	199	100
Kansas City, Mo.	64	465	160
Las Vegas, Nev.	43	553	171
Los Angeles, Calif.	40	251	127
Nashville, Tenn.	58	285	133
New York, N.Y.	75	431	215
Pittsburgh, Pa.	53	402	185
Seattle, Wash.	29	129	63
Tampa, Fla.	45	184	102
Wilmington, Del.	68	621	168

° Includes smoke, dust, and fumes and droplets of viscous liquid in air.
SOURCE: Department of Health, Education, and Welfare.

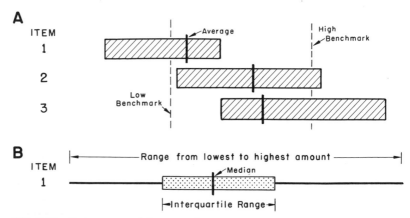

FIG. 7-28   Various uses of the range bar.

THE SLIDING-BAR CHART

The sliding-bar chart is one in which the length of a subdivided bar represents a total amount or 100 percent. One component extends to the left of a common base line, and the other to the right. These components in turn may be further subdivided, but the segments should be kept to a minimum. All segments are *positive*, as together they represent the total.

In the chart in Fig. 7-29, the total length of the bar represents the retail food dollar for selected dates. The segment to the left is what the farmer receives; the right segment portrays marketing costs. The chart shows the change from 1945 to 1964.

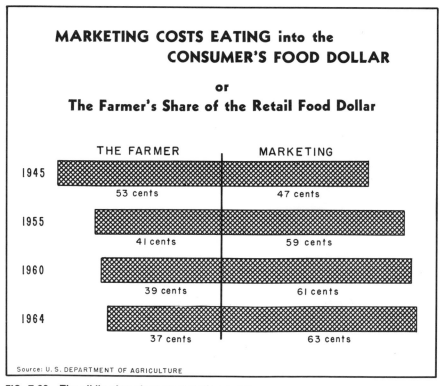

FIG. 7-29   The sliding-bar chart representing a dollar.

The length of the bar in the chart in Fig. 7-30 represents total world motor-vehicle production outside the United States. This total is divided into two categories, passenger cars, and trucks and buses. It includes only those countries that produced over 100,000 vehicles. In West Germany, truck and bus production includes about 280,000 microbuses.

These data could also be used in a grouped-bar or paired-bar chart, but those formats would not show the total. In a component-bar chart, there would be difficulty in comparing the smaller segments.

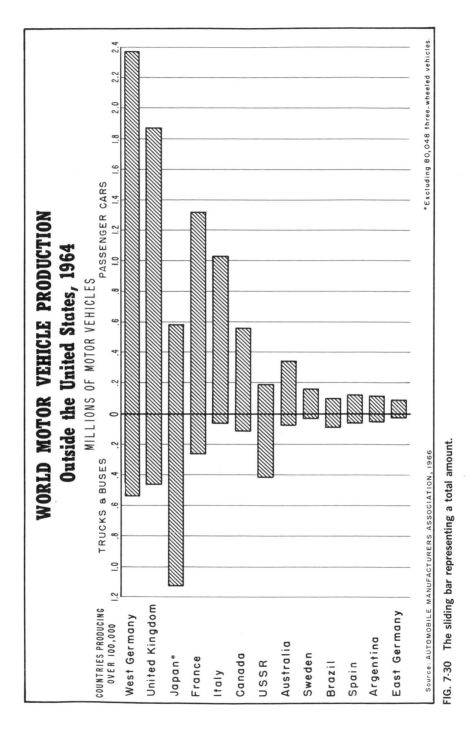

FIG. 7-30   The sliding bar representing a total amount.

POPULATION PYRAMID

The population pyramid is in effect a sliding bar, in that the total length of the bars represents the total number of persons in each age group. This length is divided by a common base line; the females are plotted to the left, and the males to the right. The chart in Fig. 7-31 further divides these segments into white and nonwhite populations.

The bars in the population pyramid are placed in juxtaposition. This type of chart, showing population and occupation statistics, is helpful in analyzing the structure of the labor force.

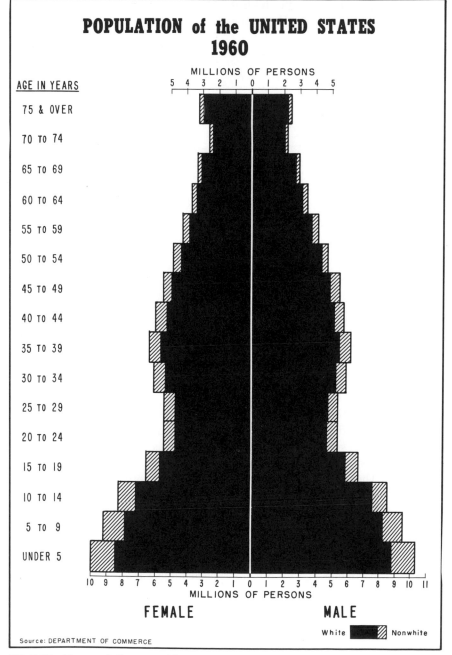

POPULATION of the UNITED STATES
1960

MILLIONS OF PERSONS

AGE IN YEARS

75 & OVER

70 TO 74

65 TO 69

60 TO 64

55 TO 59

50 TO 54

45 TO 49

40 TO 44

35 TO 39

30 TO 34

25 TO 29

20 TO 24

15 TO 19

10 TO 14

5 TO 9

UNDER 5

MILLIONS OF PERSONS

FEMALE   MALE

White   Nonwhite

Source: DEPARTMENT OF COMMERCE

FIG. 7-31   The population pyramid.

Table 7-5 begins with the 75-years-and-older group to facilitate the reading of the amounts in Fig. 7-31.

TABLE 7-5   *Population of the United States by Age, Sex, and Race, 1960 (Thousands of Persons)*

Age, years	Male		Female		Total	
	White	Nonwhite	White	Nonwhite	White	Nonwhite
75 and over	2,206	181	2,968	208	5,174	389
70–74	2,018	167	2,373	181	4,391	348
65–69	2,684	247	3,055	272	5,739	519
60–64	3,122	288	3,429	304	6,551	592
55–59	3,729	399	3,898	405	7,626	804
50–54	4,286	449	4,408	464	8,694	912
45–49	4,828	530	4,957	565	9,785	1,094
40–44	5,117	559	5.306	618	10,423	1,177
35–39	5,447	633	5,694	708	11,141	1,340
30–34	5,218	628	5,371	732	10,589	1,360
25–29	4,722	611	4,834	702	9,556	1,314
20–24	4,646	627	4,825	703	9,471	1,330
15–19	5,837	797	5,771	814	11,608	1,611
10–14	7,457	1,068	7,182	1,067	14,639	2,135
5–9	8,202	1,302	7,885	1,302	16,088	2,604
Under 5	8,849	1,481	8,509	1,482	17,359	2,962

SOURCE: U.S. Department of Commerce, Bureau of the Census.

Selective Service at one time made use of a basic population chart depicting male and female persons in the United States. This chart was mounted in a permanent frame at the top of which were hooks where we could hang transparent overlays (see Fig. 1-9). These overlays portrayed the number of persons in the labor force by industry and age groups. From this and other pertinent overlays, it was determined where to draw needed military personnel so as not to hold up the manufacture of durable and nondurable goods or farm production.

Many uses can be made of such a basic chart by dwelling on particular age groups for special subject matter.

POPULATION PROFILE

The bars in Fig. 7-32 are not sliding bars, as the left and right segments do not equal a total. The bars on the left represent the population in 1940, and those on the right the 1960 population. The connected bars form a bar-profile chart.

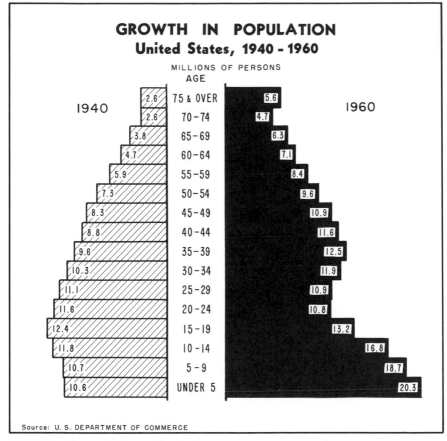

FIG. 7-32   The population-profile chart.

EIGHT

Other Graphic Forms

THE PIE OR SECTOR CHART

The pie or sector chart is a circle whose area is divided into component parts. This type of chart makes a comparison of these segments and shows their relation to the whole. It should be used sparingly, especially when there are many components. It is not only difficult to compare area segments accurately, but most difficult to label them properly.

Figure 8-1 shows the food dollar plotted as a pie chart and a bar chart. The pie chart shows the relation of the cost of various foods to the dollar, while the bar chart compares the actual amounts in cents. A component 100 percent bar, representing the dollar, could have been plotted from the same data. When made in a step format similar to Fig. 7-18, there would be no difficulty in the labeling.

In the chart in Fig. 8-2, the percentages can readily be compared visually, as the segments are few, well defined, and clearly labeled. The chart shows the percent increase of rail shipments of fresh fruits and vegetables from the California-Arizona area over a ten-year period.

233

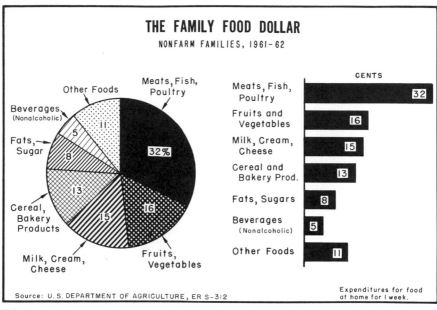

FIG. 8-1   Pie versus bar chart.

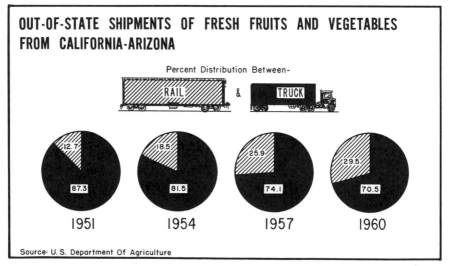

FIG. 8-2   The pie or sector chart.

When two or more pie charts are compared, keep the *patterns* of the segments in the same order. This more readily shows their differences. Plot the values clockwise. By starting the plotting from this common point, the segments are more quickly identified (see Fig. 8-3).

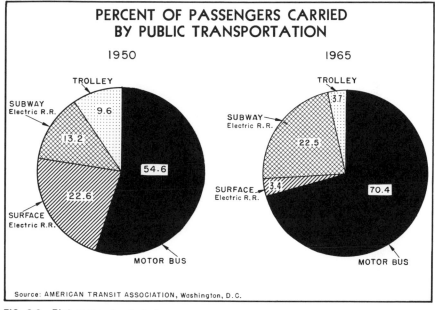

FIG. 8-3   **Plot segments clockwise.**

PIE AND TREND

A simple pie chart is often used in conjunction with other types of charts. Figure 8-4 shows a pie chart closely related to a line chart. The curves give the trend shift in population in Washington County, Maryland, while the pie chart shows the percentage change in the total shift for each ten-year period. The legend for the segments is carried on the first circle.

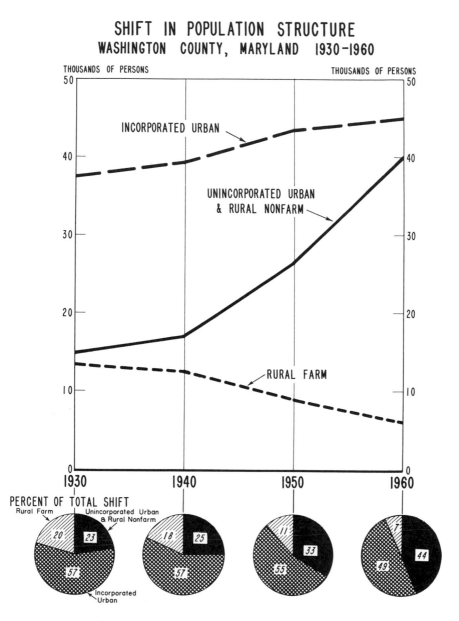

SHIFT IN POPULATION STRUCTURE
WASHINGTON COUNTY, MARYLAND 1930–1960

FIG. 8-4 Combining pie and trends.

PIE AND COLUMN

The 100 percent column in Fig. 8-5 represents the kind of degree held among educational-television personnel. The segments in the pie charts show the major areas studied to obtain each kind of degree.

Humanities and other studies played a large part in each group, but the area of education had the highest percent studying for the doctorate.

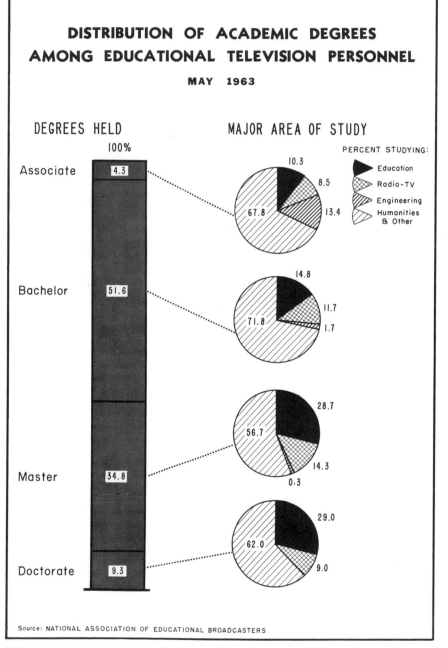

DISTRIBUTION OF ACADEMIC DEGREES AMONG EDUCATIONAL TELEVISION PERSONNEL

MAY 1963

DEGREES HELD

100%

Associate 4.3

Bachelor 51.6

Master 34.8

Doctorate 9.3

MAJOR AREA OF STUDY

PERCENT STUDYING:
- Education
- Radio-TV
- Engineering
- Humanities & Other

10.3
8.5
13.4
67.8

14.8
11.7
1.7
71.8

28.7
14.3
0.3
56.7

29.0
9.0
62.0

Source: NATIONAL ASSOCIATION OF EDUCATIONAL BROADCASTERS

FIG. 8-5 Combining pie and column.

CIRCLES OF VARIOUS SIZE

It is much more difficult to compare sizes of circles than it is to read differences in the lengths of bars and columns. Figure 8-6 is not a pie chart, but circles where *areas* are to be compared. If it were not for the percents lettered by the circles, this comparison would mean little.

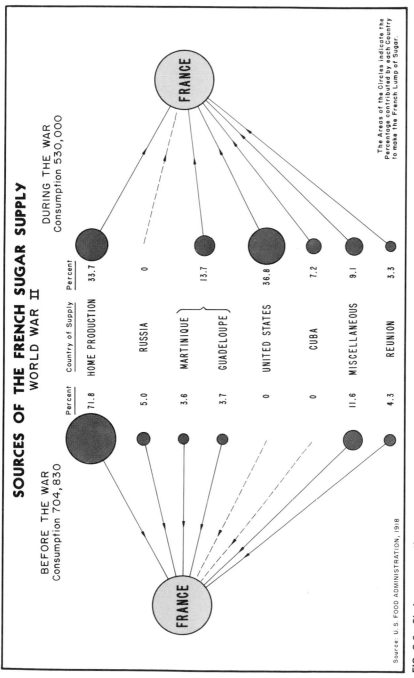

FIG. 8-6   Circles representing areas.

CALCULATING DIAMETERS

When drafting circles of different sizes, the common error is to make their diameters proportional to the *size* of the data, instead of calculating their *areas*. The space allotted the drawing in a *planned* layout must be considered. Assume that the *largest* circle can have a 4-in. diameter.

For drafting purposes a simple method for obtaining other diameters is to:

1. Divide the smaller amounts by the largest amount in the data. Carry the quotient to a two-digit decimal.

2. Find the square root of the quotient (see Table 8-1).

TABLE 8-1   *Use for Drafting Diameters of Small Circles—Square Roots of Decimals 0.01–0.99*

Decimal	Sq Root	Decimal	Sq Root	Decimal	Sq Root	Decimal	Sq Root
. . .	. . .	0.25	0.500	0.50	0.707	0.75	0.866
0.01	0.100	0.26	0.510	0.51	0.714	0.76	0.872
0.02	0.141	0.27	0.520	0.52	0.721	0.77	0.878
0.03	0.173	0.28	0.529	0.53	0.728	0.78	0.883
0.04	0.200	0.29	0.539	0.54	0.735	0.79	0.889
0.05	0.224	0.30	0.548	0.55	0.742	0.80	0.894
0.06	0.245	0.31	0.557	0.56	0.748	0.81	0.900
0.07	0.265	0.32	0.566	0.57	0.755	0.82	0.906
0.08	0.283	0.33	0.575	0.58	0.762	0.83	0.911
0.09	0.300	0.34	0.583	0.59	0.768	0.84	0.917
0.10	0.316	0.35	0.592	0.60	0.775	0.85	0.922
0.11	0.332	0.36	0.600	0.61	0.781	0.86	0.927
0.12	0.346	0.37	0.608	0.62	0.787	0.87	0.933
0.13	0.361	0.38	0.616	0.63	0.794	0.88	0.938
0.14	0.374	0.39	0.625	0.64	0.800	0.89	0.943
0.15	0.387	0.40	0.633	0.65	0.806	0.90	0.949
0.16	0.400	0.41	0.640	0.66	0.812	0.91	0.954
0.17	0.412	0.42	0.648	0.67	0.819	0.92	0.959
0.18	0.424	0.43	0.656	0.68	0.825	0.93	0.964
0.19	0.436	0.44	0.663	0.69	0.831	0.94	0.970
0.20	0.447	0.45	0.671	0.70	0.837	0.95	0.975
0.21	0.458	0.46	0.678	0.71	0.843	0.96	0.980
0.22	0.469	0.47	0.686	0.72	0.849	0.97	0.985
0.23	0.480	0.48	0.693	0.73	0.854	0.98	0.990
0.24	0.490	0.49	0.700	0.74	0.860	0.99	0.995

3. Multiply the square root by the predetermined diameter of the largest circle. This gives the diameter of the smaller circles.

For example, using 4 in. as the largest predetermined diameter representing $142 (see Table 8-2):

1. Amount b, $98, divided by $142 = 0.69
2. The square root of 0.69 = 0.831
3. 0.831 $\times$ 4 in. = 3.3 in., the diameter of the b circle.

Follow the same method for determining the other diameters. Drafted diameters for Table 8-2 are shown in Fig. 8-7A.

TABLE 8-2   *Calculating Diameters When Largest Diameter Is Known*

Circle	Amount	Quotient (col. 1 ÷ 142)	Square root of col. 2	Diameter (col. 3 × 4 in.°)
a	$142	. . .	. . .	4.0°
b	98	0.69	0.831	3.3
c	53	0.37	0.608	2.4
d	30	0.21	0.458	1.8
e	18	0.13	0.361	1.4

° Predetermined largest diameter (see Fig. 8-7 and text).

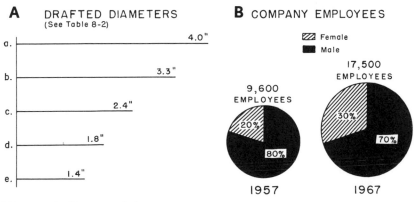

A   DRAFTED DIAMETERS
(See Table 8-2)

a. ———— 4.0"
b. ———— 3.3"
c. ———— 2.4"
d. ———— 1.8"
e. ———— 1.4"

B COMPANY EMPLOYEES

Female
Male

9,600 EMPLOYEES
20%
80%
1957

17,500 EMPLOYEES
30%
70%
1967

FIG. 8-7   Drafting area circles.

SEGMENTS IN VARYING CIRCLES

Circles of various sizes may be divided into segments. In this case each circle, no matter what its area, represents 100 percent (see Fig. 8-7B). Where possible, letter data in or near segments; otherwise a legend must be carried. This type of pictorial is often used on maps.

For popular presentations it is advisable not to indulge profusely in area, volume, or three-dimensional charts (see Fig. 2-22). These may appear to be more interesting and a relief from the standard chart, but are too apt to be misread visually. There are many ways that a straightforward, meaningful presentation may hold attention through its shading, color, lettering, and illustrations. But simplicity in presentation facilitates retention of the message.

THE STEREOGRAM

Figure 8-8 is an example of a tridimensional representation, the stereogram. It was made, for this publication, by Prof. Dr. Fernando Pedroni, Università degli Studi di Roma.

The stereogram pictured was formed by following an extension of the system of Cartesian axes to the three dimensions of space; that is, to the two coordinates of the plane (axis of ordinate or Y axis and axis of abscissa or X axis, see Fig. 4-1), a third coordinate of *elevation* or Z axis, originating from the point of junction or origin of the first two coordinates, was added.

In the collapsible model shown, the three variables plotted are age of male population, census years, and percent of males in age groups.

The number of males by age groups for *each* census year was plotted individually on cross-section paper. Their silhouettes were cut out and hinged parallel to each other on the upright stiff board. This cardboard had been lettered and spaced accurately for census years, and with a percentage scale to denote the percent of males in the age groups.

The trend of the percent of males, beginning with the youngest age group, was plotted directly on the board. The other percentages were plotted separately on cross-section paper and their trends cut out in profile.

To interlock the plotted strips, the hinged strips were cut halfway down through their upper halves at the points where the crosswise

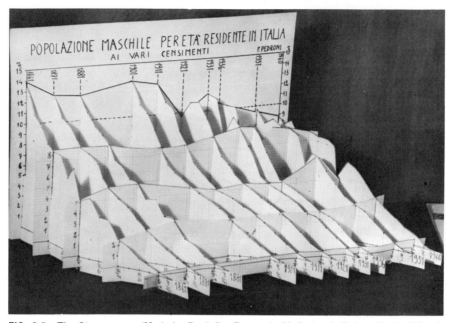

FIG. 8-8   The Stereogram. (Made by Prof. Dr. Fernando M. Pedroni, Università degli Studi di Roma, Italy.)

strips intersect. These latter strips had corresponding slits halfway up from the bottoms. When the two sets were fitted together at the points of intersection, they formed a rigid but collapsible stereogram whose continuous surface gives a clear idea of the movement of the three variables.

This type of model, collapsing sideways, may be folded up or expanded at will. When folded, it is flat and can be easily carried or filed. Open, it can stand unsupported and graphically portray three physical dimensions in space.

Professor Pedroni's book, *Rappresentazioni Statistiche*, 4th ed., Ulrico Hoepli, Milan, Italy, 1967, has been revised and enlarged.

Should the plottings of the data be somewhat erratic, with several points not clearly visible, the trends of the model could be made of clear acetate. Binding the horizontal curves with very narrow tapes of different colors and the vertical curves in black or a neutral color would allow a visual reading of the lower plotted points. The vertical trends could be attached to the back supporting board with transparent tape.

THE COSMOGRAPH

The term cosmograph applies both to the manufactured mechanical device and to the graphic chart which shows counterbalancing items and their distribution.

The mechanical device produces a graphic analysis of data by means of a black background board on which 1,000 strips of white paper have been securely fastened. These strips form a 100 percent column. They are separated by clamps into groups representing the desired percentages of the data.

The same principle is shown in the cosmograph chart format, Fig. 8-9. The stack of dollars forms a 100 percent column. The segments spreading fanlike to the left and right show where the money came from and where it went.

This graphic form is especially useful in portraying income and expenditures; payroll and payroll distribution; sales by territory and by salesmen; finished stock inventory and sales; assets and liabilities; and status reports.

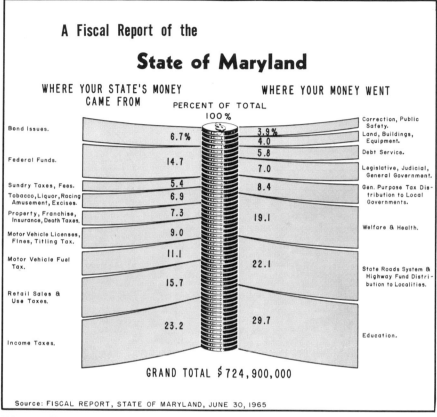

FIG. 8-9   The cosmograph.

THE PROFILE CHART

The profile chart is usually used to depict the price direction of the majority of common stocks at the close of the year. Figure 8-10 shows that in 1959 more issues were up than down, while the 1960 profile is almost the reverse picture.

In 1961 (not plotted), 891—or the bulk of the issues—were up, and only 183 were down. This is one of the indications that all stocks do not move in unison. It is best for investors to investigate before investing.

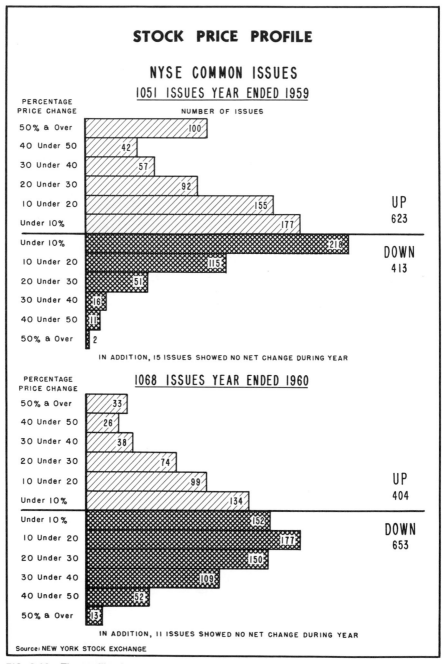

FIG. 8-10 The profile chart.

THE SILHOUETTE CHART

The silhouette chart can serve as a pattern for future projects. By analyzing the new project, one can estimate whether there are enough employees on hand for specified jobs or whether more should be taken on. The time element is the deciding factor for hiring (see Fig. 8-11).

Plotting the silhouette gives a fair picture of when employees should be on hand for specified work in order to meet the completion date. Types of jobs may change, but a fair estimate can be set up by visually laying out the project for hiring and timing.

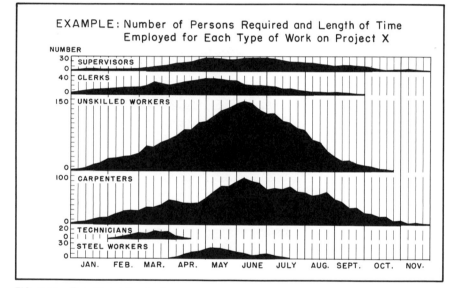

FIG. 8-11   The silhouette chart.

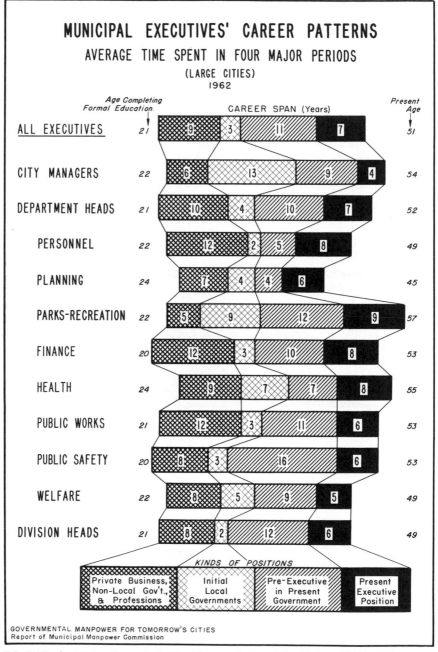

FIG. 8-12 A career pattern chart. (Used by permission of the McGraw-Hill Book Company, New York.)

A CAREER PATTERN

Figure 8-12 is from *Government Manpower for Tomorrow's Cities*, a report of the Municipal Manpower Commission. A pattern is formed by this layout, from which career mobility into high municipal positions can be examined.

The career-span age is shown by the total length of the bar in each executive group. The figures at the ends of the bars represent executive's ages at the start of their careers and their ages at time of the survey. The components of each bar show four major periods of their careers.

In laying out the chart, total coverage of age in career span was first considered. This was plotted from the scale drawn at an angle, as seen in Fig. 8-13. The scale starts at twenty, the youngest age completing formal education, and ends at fifty-seven, the oldest present age. Each bar was then divided into the number of years in positions of their career pattern. Plottings were measured from the horizontal scale in Fig. 8-13.

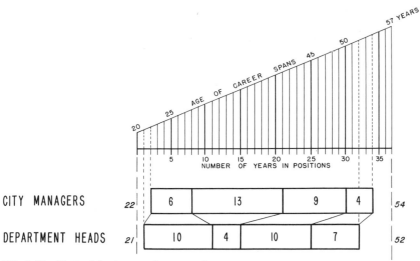

FIG. 8-13 Method for layout of pattern chart.

THE RANKING CHART

Figure 8-14 graphically compares the popularity position or *rank* of automotive colors for the years 1965 and 1966.

The majority of the medium and dark colors continued at the same level of increase in customer favor. White, which was number one in 1965, gave way to medium blue in 1966. Black dropped from eighth place to thirteenth as a result of the increased popularity of dark colors generally. The greatest gain in color preference was medium brown, which jumped from thirteenth to fifth place in 1966.

The rank of cities or states may be arranged in order according to size of population. In fact, any data with a common attribute may be arranged in such a format. However, too many series should not be used, as the crisscrossing lines would become too confusing for a clear understanding.

RANK BY SHADING

The charts in Fig. 8-15 are arranged by rate of projected employment growth. Both the industries and the major occupational groups are coded by shading from decline up to more than average. The shadings indicate their rates of growth.

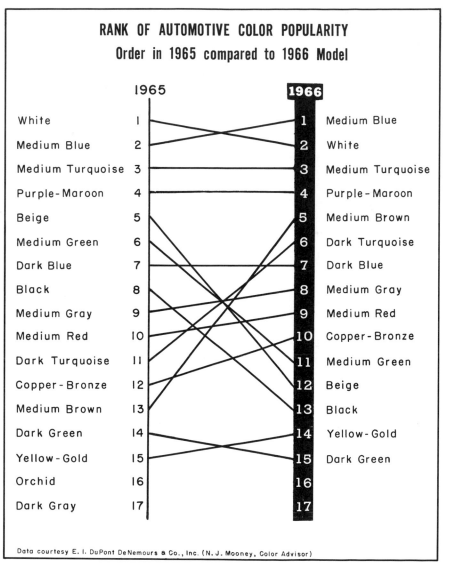

FIG. 8-14   The ranking chart.

OUTLOOK FOR OCCUPATIONAL CHANGE

While total employment will go up by 1/4 by 1975
Industry growth rates will vary widely

INDUSTRY	PROJECTED EMPLOYMENT GROWTH				
	Decline	No Change	Less than Average	Average	More than Average
Government					▨
Services					▨
Contract Construction					▨
Wholesale & Retail Trade				▨	
Finance, Insurance, & Real Estate				▨	
Manufacturing			▨		
Transportation & Public Utilities			▨		
Mining	▨				
Agriculture	▨				

Job opportunities generally will increase fastest in occupations
requiring the most education and training

MAJOR OCCUPATIONAL GROUP	PROJECTED EMPLOYMENT GROWTH				
	Decline	No Change	Less than Average	Average	More than Average
Professional, Technical, & Kindred Workers					▨
Service Workers					▨
Clerical Workers					▨
Skilled Workers				▨	
Managers, Officials, & Proprietors				▨	
Sales Workers				▨	
Semiskilled Workers			▨		
Laborers (nonfarm)		▨			
Farm Workers	▨				

Source: U.S. BUREAU OF LABOR STATISTICS

FIG. 8-15 Rank by shading.

THE GANTT CHART

Wars, because of the mass production needed, seem to bring forth new ideas for graphic presentation. The First World War educed the value of the Gantt process chart as a method to show comparison between performance and delivery. Government and military agencies found it invaluable in helping to visualize what progress was being made in filling the overwhelmingly large number of orders that were flooding the munitions and manufacturing plants.

This type of chart was not widely known at that time, but because it dealt with present performance and future expectation, it was ideal to cope with the volume of data to be handled.

PRINCIPLE OF THE GANTT CHART

The Gantt chart was named after its creater Henry Lawrence Gantt, a famous management engineer. It has manifold uses, as it can be adapted to the needs of record keeping in any plant or office where knowledge of the time element versus scheduled work to be done in a specified time is essential.

The *work-load* chart shows how much work there is ahead for the plant; the *layout* chart plans in advance the work for each machine or worker; the *machine-record* chart notes the performance of the machine; the *man-record* chart keeps track of the achievement of each individual; and the *progress* chart depicts the progress made toward the completion of a plan.

Basically the layout is simple. The chart may be divided horizontally into days, weeks, or other time periods. A light horizontal bar records the actual performance, while a heavy bar cumulates the progress on the job.

Gantt charts in a plant or office will help the executive to visualize his problems by enabling him to observe quickly the day-by-day achievements as well as new tendencies in his business. He can judge the performance of individuals and machines, keep track of the work load, spot difficulties that may be holding up the job, and note the progress being made on the project.

Such a chart not only serves the executive but gives the individual employee a chance to compare his standard of work with that of his fellow workers.

The Gantt chart became widely used during World War II in control rooms of the military and throughout industry.

THE MACHINE-RECORD CHART

On the machine-record chart the foreman can keep the daily record of the performance of the machines in his department by coding the record with symbols: *P* for power trouble, *R* for repairs, etc. He can tell at a glance the problems that are holding up the scheduled plan of operation.

In the layout of Fig. 8-16, the total department performance heads the listing. The time interval is divided for an 8-hr day, each space indicating a 2-hr period.

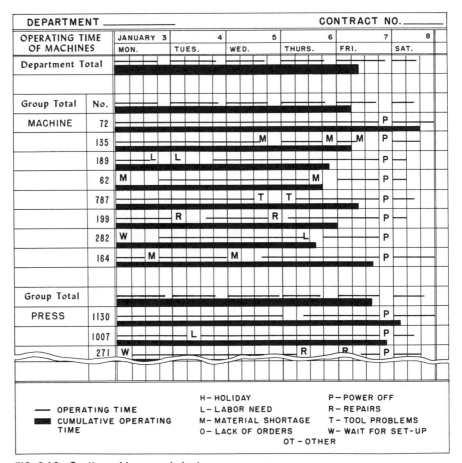

FIG. 8-16   Gantt machine-record chart.

The total department plottings are an *average* of the group plottings. In this case they were estimated, as only part of the chart is shown.

The first group total is complete. The light line shows the daily average actual running time of all the machines in that group. The heavy bar is their cumulative average time. This is followed by the daily performance and cumulative running time of each machine. The blank spaces show that the machine was not operating, and the symbols denote the reason. Care must be taken that the cumulative bar—the sum of the light bars—be drawn accurately, as an error is difficult to detect.

Table 8-3 checks the machine-group total average and individual machines. The table records only those data plotted on the chart in Fig. 8-16.

This graphic record enables the foreman to analyze visually the reason for idleness of any machines and thereby be more readily able to remedy his problems.

TABLE 8-3   *The Gantt Machine-record Chart*
Table for machine group, Fig. 8-16

Machine number			Running time, hr				Cumulative time
	Mon.	Tues.	Wed.	Thur.	Fri.	Sat.	Total
72	8	8	8	8	6	6	44
135	8	8	5	6	3	4	34
189	5	2	8	8	6	2	31
62	2	8	8	4	6	2	30
787	8	8	4	6	6	3	35
199	8	3	6	7	6	2	32
282	2	8	8	5	6	0	29
164	6	8	3	8	6	6	37
Group total	47	53	50	52	45	25	272
Average	5.9	6.6	6.3	6.5	5.6	3.1	34.0

THE MAN-RECORD CHART

The man-record chart reflects each worker's performance in relation to a predetermined quota. In the layout in Fig. 8-17, the monthly horizontal space is divided into weekly time intervals, each week representing 100 percent of the scheduled performance for that month. This is further divided into five spaces of 20 percent each.

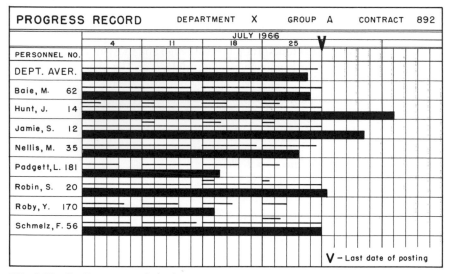

FIG. 8-17 Gantt man-record chart.

A light bar is drawn to show the actual proportion of the quota reached by the worker each week. The heavy bar immediately beneath it records the cumulative production in relation to the quota.

Thus, it shows that although M. Baie produced 80 percent of her quota the week of July 11, she was still above the department average at the last day of posting. Hunt, Jamie, Robin, and Schmelz were all well above the department average, while Roby might be considered for another type of job, as her production rate was steadily falling behind.

The second light line above the workers' record shows their cumulative percentage of work for that week. The heavy V at the end of the month denotes the last date of posting. Any difficulty, such as machine breakdown, waiting for supplies, absence, may be coded similar to the machine-record chart.

THE PERT CHART

In the 1960s a new format was developed called the PERT chart. PERT stands for Program Evaluation and Review Technique. The concept was started for government programs but is being used widely by industry and management. The basic approach is founded on the technique of networking. This network integrates in schematic form all the activities and events that must be completed or accomplished to reach a planned program's objective.

The PERT method is one used more for analysis purposes than for popular presentation. For those interested, an informative book on the subject of PERT management systems is *Schedule, Cost, and Profit Control with PERT* by Robert W. Miller, McGraw-Hill Book Company, New York, 1963. It shows how PERT methods are being utilized in commercial, industrial, and other economic planning and control activities. Figure 8-18 is a redrawing of a sample network taken from the book.

The Gantt chart is often used to summarize PERT information when a viewer may not be familiar with the network layout.

THE PROCESS-FLOW CHART

A process-flow chart shows the movement of the flow of work, as in Fig. 8-19. Three printing processes are shown by a general view of the steps that the copy passes through to completion.

This work-flow chart is used for manufacturing processes from the making of steel to the making of a shirt. Each step in the making of the product is shown as it passes through different departments or processes to the finished product.

An industry introducing a new product can visually show the path the process takes by drawing, cartooning, or illustrating the planning, the research, the special machinery needed, the tests made, the product in final form, its introduction to the market, and even consumer reports.

An excellent pictorial process-flow chart was published showing the making of tin plate from slabs. It pictured in simple outline drawings the steps taken in the hot-strip mill, the continuous pickler, the continuous cold-reducing mill, the electrolytic cleaner, the annealing furnace, the temper-pass mill, the shearing line, the white pickler, the tinning machine, the assorting room, and finally the shipping room. A brief description of the process at each step was printed under the drawings.

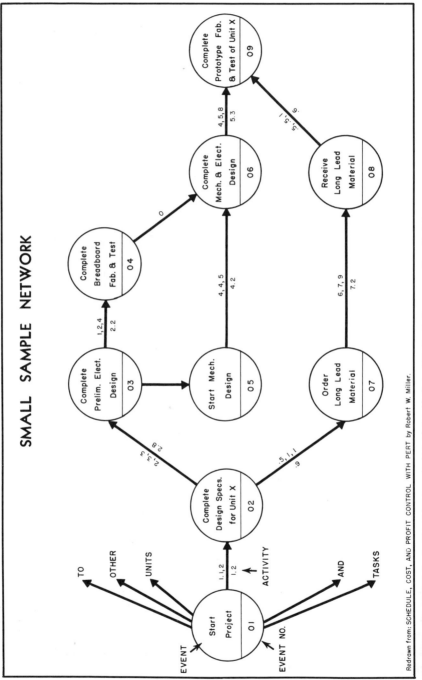

SMALL SAMPLE NETWORK

Redrawn from: SCHEDULE, COST, AND PROFIT CONTROL WITH PERT by Robert W. Miller.

FIG. 8-18   The PERT chart. (Used by permission of the McGraw-Hill Book Company, New York.)

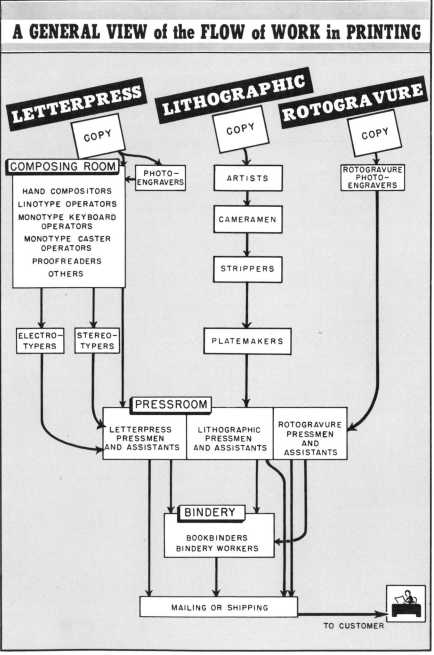

FIG. 8-19   Process-flow chart.

ACTION-FLOW CHART

Figure 8-20 shows the flow of action when a bill reaches the Senate. This is one of four layouts portraying what happens to a bill from the time it is first introduced. The action takes place in the House, the Senate, the Congressional Conference Committee, and the bill is finally presented to the President for his approval or disapproval. If he signs the act, it becomes the law of the land. The flow is clearly defined in each chart, step by step, by the numbered directional lines. The accompanying text explains each action.

This type of flow chart is used to excellent advantage in explaining a flow of action when there are many alternatives. A verbal description may prove tedious and hard to follow without a visual presentation.

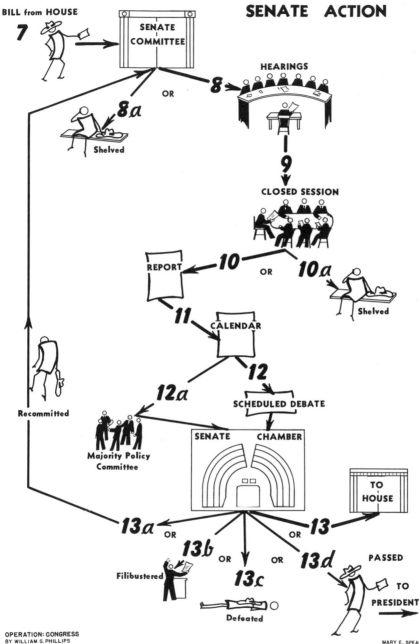

FIG. 8-20   Action-flow chart.

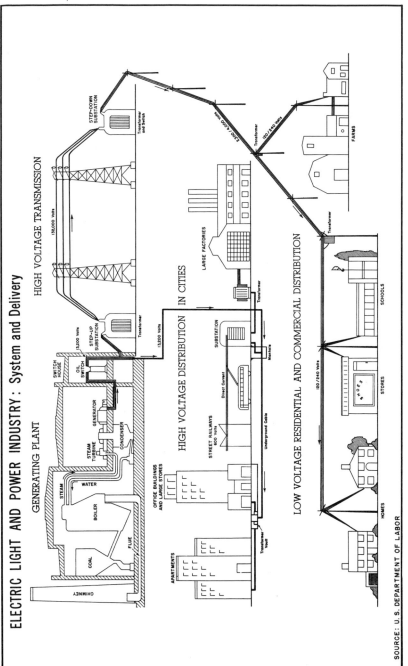

FIG. 8-21 Diagram of system operations.

DIAGRAMS

The diagram takes the form of a schematic drawing or illustration. Figure 8-21 is a simplified layout of the more important steps in the distribution of electric power in the city and on the farm. Charts were drawn to go with the diagram portraying the increase of employment and plans for future growth in the industry.

The diagram and charts show objectively how widespread the job opportunities are in the electric light and power industry. They show how the industry created employment not only in the administrative, technical, and commercial branches but also in transmission and distribution, generating, maintenance and custodial, and customer servicing. A short statement was on the broadside to this effect.

A flow diagram may show a series of separate and, in some cases, extremely complicated chemical or other manufacturing processes. Each step, represented by a simplified diagram showing the flow of the products or elements, may be traced to the climax.

A diagram may also be used to delineate how a specific piece of machinery works, by labeling each part or giving its function (see Fig. 8-22).

INJECTION MOLDING

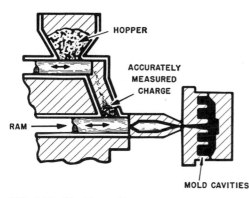

FIG. 8-22   Machinery diagram.

THE ORGANIZATION CHART

An organization chart may serve several purposes. It is a means of visually communicating to those outside the organization the nature and structure of a business and pertinent facts pertaining to it. To those inside the company, it shows who is in authority, flow of work, and functions of departments and divisions.

Those at the head of an organization are the president, vice-presidents, and other company officials. They are the ones who set the company goals, make major decisions in policies, and coordinate company activities. Their plans, in turn, are usually carried out with the assistance of management-level workers who direct the work of the various departments. As supervisors they are responsible for keeping the divisions in their department at peak efficiency and in accordance with the broad policies established for the company (see Fig. 8-23).

In smaller companies, the officials may also carry through the plans which they have developed, taking a direct part in the functions, employee relationships, and financial reports.

Not all organization charts need be for public circulation. Some are made for an analysis of the structure of the company. It will be found that the actual planning of the chart may reveal deficiencies in the setup of the organization. It can show where reorganization can do away with duplication of work, where too many employees in one section can be used to better advantage in another, where possible shortcuts or rerouting of work may be more efficient.

Those charts denoting salaries, grades, or personal facts that might cause friction should not, perhaps, be made public. But on the whole, some form of an organization chart should be made to show the purpose of the business. It would be meaningful not only to top ranking personnel but to all employees.

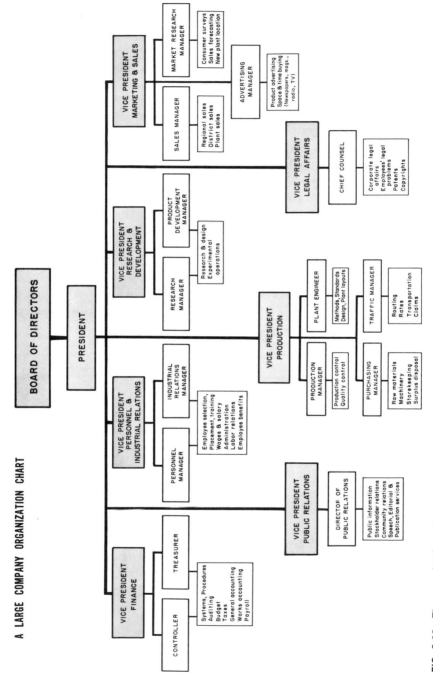

FIG. 8-23 The organization chart.

THE FUNCTIONAL ORGANIZATION CHART

The functional organization chart shows the duties and responsibilities of departments or positions, as in Fig. 8-24. In this layout the director of research not only is responsible for independent research, but keeps an eye on all research.

One government office that held a series of training programs primarily for foreign trainees set up a large organization chart, with photographs of the chief executive and heads of divisions who were to be speakers at the meetings. This tended to lend a friendlier atmosphere to the sessions. There was no guessing about who was sitting in the guest chair.

The way the trainees gathered around the chart before the meeting was interesting. If the speaker was early, some would introduce themselves and identify their countries. A brief description of the functions of each division was under the photographs to prepare the trainees for the subject of that day's meeting.

The same idea could be used in a business meeting for an employee group or regional sessions. People like to know for whom they are working. It makes them feel more a part of the organization.

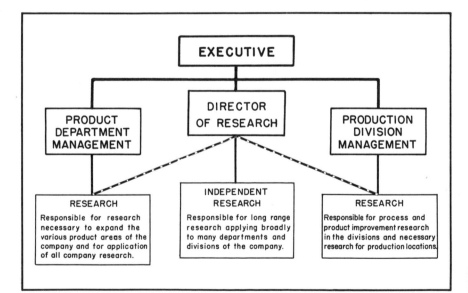

FIG. 8-24   Functional organization chart.

THE BROADSIDE ORGANIZATION CHART

Figure 8-25 gives a general picture of job opportunities in a department store. This is a poster-type layout that does not go into a detailed description of the positions, but uses illustrations to depict the jobs.

This chart calls attention to the fact that there are varied jobs in a department store and that all opportunities are not in the buying and selling end.

COUNTY GOVERNMENT ORGANIZATION CHART

The four major types of executive-administrative structures now in use in county government are distinguished primarily by the nature of executive authority and by executive-legislative relationships (see Fig. 8-26). These types may either replace or operate in conjunction with the commission system, and are most frequently classified as:

A. Council—Elective Executive

B. Council—Elective Executive—Professional Administrator

C. Council—Professional Administrator

D. Council—Manager

The first two forms emphasize executive independence and leadership in all governmental activities, while the second two emphasize legislative leadership in policy formulation, with the assistance of trained staff personnel. All have in common the transfer of certain functions from the legislative body to an executive or administrator.

Details of the systems and how they vary are given in the final report, *Responsibility, Opportunity, Challenge* of the Washington County Study Commission, Hagerstown, Maryland, 1963.

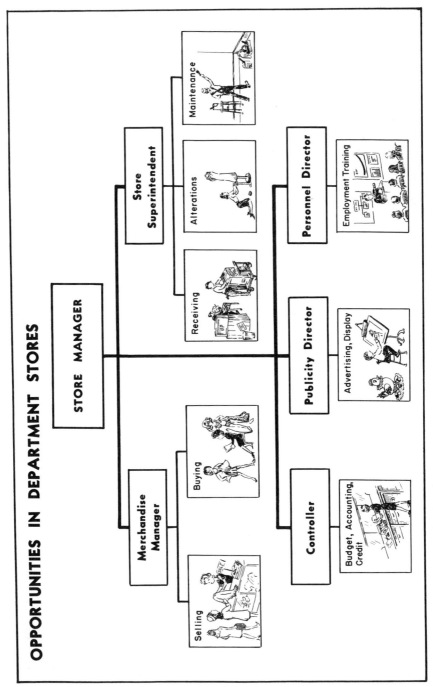

FIG. 8-25   Illustrating the organization chart.

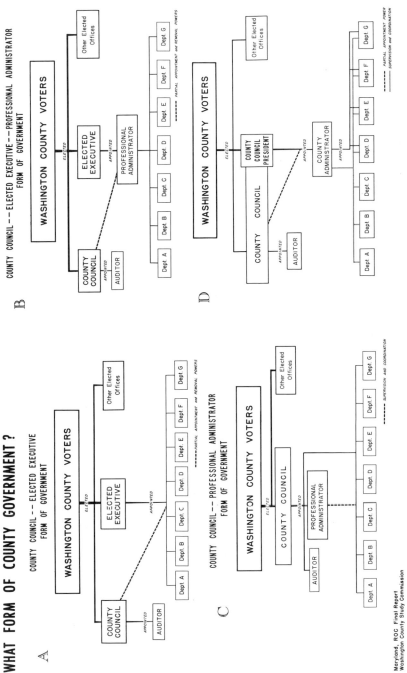

WHAT FORM OF COUNTY GOVERNMENT ?

A

COUNTY COUNCIL -- ELECTED EXECUTIVE
FORM OF GOVERNMENT

WASHINGTON COUNTY VOTERS

ELECTED — Other Elected Offices

ELECTED EXECUTIVE

COUNTY COUNCIL

APPOINTED — AUDITOR

APPOINTED

Dept. A | Dept. B | Dept. C | Dept. D | Dept. E | Dept. F | Dept. G

------ PARTIAL APPOINTMENT and REMOVAL POWERS

B

COUNTY COUNCIL -- ELECTED EXECUTIVE -- PROFESSIONAL ADMINISTRATOR
FORM OF GOVERNMENT

WASHINGTON COUNTY VOTERS

ELECTED — Other Elected Offices

ELECTED EXECUTIVE

COUNTY COUNCIL

APPOINTED — AUDITOR

PROFESSIONAL ADMINISTRATOR

APPOINTED

Dept. A | Dept. B | Dept. C | Dept. D | Dept. E | Dept. F | Dept. G

------ PARTIAL APPOINTMENT and REMOVAL POWERS

C

COUNTY COUNCIL -- PROFESSIONAL ADMINISTRATOR
FORM OF GOVERNMENT

WASHINGTON COUNTY VOTERS

ELECTED — Other Elected Offices

COUNTY COUNCIL

APPOINTED

AUDITOR

PROFESSIONAL ADMINISTRATOR

Dept. A | Dept. B | Dept. C | Dept. D | Dept. E | Dept. F | Dept. G

------ SUPERVISION AND COORDINATION

D

WASHINGTON COUNTY VOTERS

ELECTED — Other Elected Offices

COUNTY COUNCIL PRESIDENT

COUNTY COUNCIL

APPOINTED — AUDITOR

COUNTY ADMINISTRATOR

APPOINTED

Dept. A | Dept. B | Dept. C | Dept. D | Dept. E | Dept. F | Dept. G

------ PARTIAL APPOINTMENT POWER
------ SUPERVISION and COORDINATION

Maryland, ROC Final Report
Washington County Study Commission

FIG. 8-26 Four forms of county government.

DRAFTING ORGANIZATION CHARTS

In the construction of the organization chart, the flow line of authority should diminish in weight as the order of responsibility branches downward. Make all flow lines of *greater* width than the outline of the boxes. The eye can then follow the progression of the chart without interruption.

MAGNETS AND CARDBOARD

One way to dramatize an objective of a chart is to put some unexpected movement in it. I have made use of magnets to do this. A two-trend chart was laid out on black cardboard, about 12 by 15 in. The grid and lettering were in white, while one trend was of light blue tape and the other of chrome yellow. Using two magnets, I glued a black arrow, heavily outlined in white, to the magnet to be used on the chart side of the board. The other magnet, glued in a $\frac{3}{4}$-in. wooden strip, could be easily handled in back of the board.

Propping the cardboard firmly and seeing that the magnets were attracted, I could move the one back of the board in such a manner that the arrow would point out each step that I wanted to emphasize. With practice you will learn to remove the arrow, magnet *first*, so it won't drop off.

This produces a surprising effect when first seen, as many do not know that magnets can be attracted through cardboard. A lot could be done with pictograms using this method.

MAGNETIC BOARDS AND ACCESSORIES

Different types of magnetic control boards and accessories may be purchased that will meet almost every need. Figure 8-27 shows a magnetic kit assembled. It pictures a $25\frac{1}{2}$ by $37\frac{1}{2}$-in. green magnetic chalkboard in an aluminum frame. The kit includes sets of four-line information cards, clear acetate magnetic holders, $\frac{3}{4}$-in. condensed white letters, and white and yellow magnetic ribbon. It serves as a visual control unit and can give you up-to-the-minute information.

Other boards are ruled for daily projects, month-by-month yearly schedules, and other layouts, or you can rule your own board. Magnetic symbols, letters, numbers, strips, clips, and other magnetic accessories are obtainable.

FIG. 8-27   Magnetic Chart Board. (Madison A-V Company, New York.)

NINE

The Map Chart

Maps always attract attention. They have a personal meaning for everyone. After reading the title, without being aware of it, you are apt to look first for your state or country or places you have visited or read about. Thus, the map chart should be used only when geographic information is of paramount importance and when the data can be readily and correctly interpreted in this form.

Such a chart is easily read when depicting courses on routing or flow maps of travel, transportation, navigation, communication, pipelines, etc., and on surface maps showing weather, location of natural resources, properties, and similar subjects where geographic surfaces are involved.

Figure 9-1 is a simple and direct comparison of the size of Alaska in relation to the United States. It shows definitely that Alaska is now our largest state.

However, when the information on the map depicts statistical data or economic situations, the map chart must not only locate the story but portray the message in the type of map most suitable for the facts.

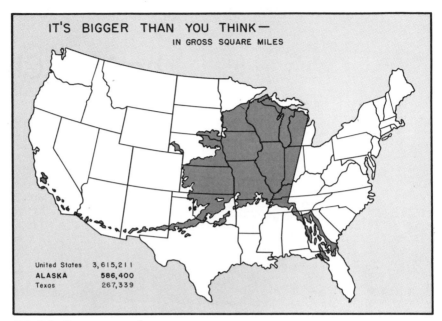

FIG. 9-1   An area comparison.

THE SHADED MAP

When the popular multishaded map representation is used, the data must refer directly to the *areas* to be shaded. The misreading of *nonarea* data is mainly due to the fact that even though a large area and a small area bear the same shading, they do not visually assume the same magnitude.

Should a more decisive comparison of the statistical map data be needed, draft a multiple-bar chart as in Figs. 7-4 or 7-5.

QUANTITATIVE MAPS

The *quantitative* crosshatched map is especially suited for the presentation of rates, ratios, and frequency-distribution data relative to areas. The shadings or patterns identify, by order of intensity, in which numerical or percentage group each state or area belongs. The map in Fig. 9-2 shows the percentage change in the population of the United States from 1950 to 1960. There was a decrease in Arkansas, District of Columbia, and West Virginia.

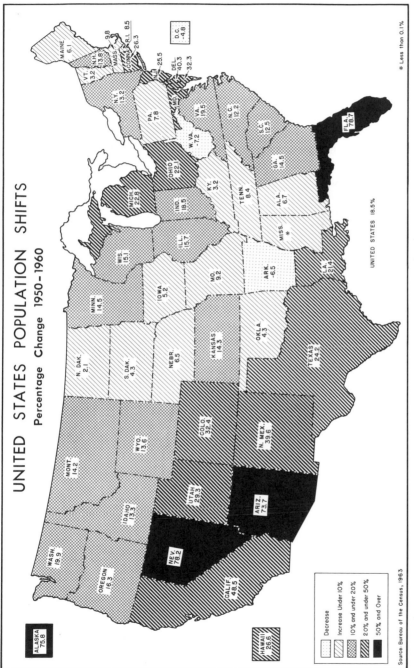

UNITED STATES POPULATION SHIFTS
Percentage Change 1950–1960

ALASKA
75.8

MAINE
6.1

N.H.
13.8

VT.
13.2

MASS.
9.8

CONN.
26.3

R.I.
8.5

N.Y.
13.2

N.J.
25.5

PA.
7.8

DEL.
40.3

MD.
32.3

D.C.
-4.8

W. VA.
-7.2

VA.
19.5

N.C.
12.2

S.C.
12.5

OHIO
22.1

KY.
3.2

TENN.
8.4

GA.
14.5

ALA.
6.7

FLA.
78.7

MICH.
22.8

IND.
18.5

ILL.
15.7

MISS.
*

WIS.
15.1

MO.
9.2

ARK.
-6.5

LA.
21.4

MINN.
14.5

IOWA
5.2

N. DAK.
2.1

S. DAK.
4.3

NEBR.
6.5

KANSAS
14.3

OKLA.
4.3

TEXAS
24.2

COLO.
32.4

N. MEX.
39.6

MONT.
14.2

WYO.
13.6

IDAHO
13.3

UTAH
29.3

ARIZ.
73.7

NEV.
78.2

WASH.
19.9

OREGON
16.3

CALIF.
48.5

UNITED STATES 18.5%

* Less than 0.1%

HAWAII
26.6

Decrease

Increase Under 10%

10% and under 20%

20% and under 50%

50% and Over

Source: Bureau of the Census, 1963

FIG. 9-2 The shaded quantitative map.

ARRANGING THE DISTRIBUTION OF DATA

The grouping of the intervals to be represented by gradations of shading is important. It tends to affect the visual impression of the map.

Aim to keep groups to four or five shadings. At the same time try to keep the number of items in each group of a near-equal size. Too many shadings are difficult to remember when referring back and forth from legend to map. They should run progressively from light to dark, depending upon the emphasis desired in the data.

Table 9-1A lists the states in alphabetical order. To more easily decide how to group the distribution intervals, arrange the data in numerical order as in Table 9-1B.

TABLE 9-1A   *United States Population Shifts, 1950–1960 (Percentage Increase or Decrease)*

	Percentage		Percentage
United States	18.5	Missouri	9.2
Alabama	6.7	Montana	14.2
Alaska	75.8	Nebraska	6.5
Arizona	73.7	Nevada	78.2
Arkansas	−6.5	New Hampshire	13.8
California	48.5	New Jersey	25.5
Colorado	32.4	New Mexico	39.6
Connecticut	26.3	New York	13.2
Delaware	40.3	North Carolina	12.2
District of Columbia	−4.8	North Dakota	2.1
Florida	78.7	Ohio	22.1
Georgia	14.5	Oklahoma	4.3
Hawaii	26.6	Oregon	16.3
Idaho	13.3	Pennsylvania	7.8
Illinois	15.7	Rhode Island	8.5
Indiana	18.5	South Carolina	12.5
Iowa	5.2	South Dakota	4.3
Kansas	14.3	Tennessee	8.4
Kentucky	3.2	Texas	24.2
Louisiana	21.4	Utah	29.3
Maine	6.1	Vermont	3.2
Maryland	32.3	Virginia	19.5
Massachusetts	9.8	Washington	19.9
Michigan	22.8	West Virginia	−7.2
Minnesota	14.5	Wisconsin	15.1
Mississippi°	. . .	Wyoming	13.6

° Less than 0.1%.

SOURCE: U.S. Bureau of Census, 1967.

TABLE 9-1B   *Table Arranged Numerically to Determine
Interval Groupings for Shading on Map 9-2*

Decrease			
West Virginia	−7.2	Kansas	14.3
Arkansas	−6.5	Georgia	14.5
District of Columbia	−4.8	Minnesota	14.5
		Wisconsin	15.1
Increase under 10%		Illinois	15.7
Mississippi°	. . .	Oregon	16.3
North Dakota	2.1	Indiana	18.5
Kentucky	3.2	Virginia	19.5
Vermont	3.2	Washington	19.9
Oklahoma	4.3		
South Dakota	4.3	*20% and under 50%*	
Iowa	5.2	Louisiana	21.4
Maine	6.1	Ohio	22.1
Nebraska	6.5	Michigan	22.8
Alabama	6.7	Texas	24.2
Pennsylvania	7.8	New Jersey	25.5
Tennessee	8.4	Connecticut	26.3
Rhode Island	8.5	Hawaii	26.6
Missouri	9.2	Utah	29.3
Massachusetts	9.8	Maryland	32.3
		Colorado	32.4
10% and under 20%		New Mexico	39.6
North Carolina	12.2	Delaware	40.3
South Carolina	12.5	California	48.5
New York	13.2		
Idaho	13.3	*50% and over*	
Wyoming	13.6	Arizona	73.7
New Hampshire	13.8	Alaska	75.8
Montana	14.2	Nevada	78.2
		Florida	78.7

° Less than 0.1%.

A closer breakdown of the "20 percent and under 50 percent"
would obviously require more shading patterns, i.e., one pattern
each for "20 percent and under 30 percent," "30 percent and under
40 percent," "40 percent and over." Also the number of items in
each group would be of uneven distribution.

METHODS OF SHADING

Shading and crosshatching comes in commercially printed patterns, chemically prepared papers, or film overlays. Some are
wax-backed or pressure-sensitive for adhering to the map.

Should wax adhere to patterns already applied, it can be removed easily with a rubber-cement pickup. This is a crepe latex that lifts up and removes dried rubber cement and most other adhesives from working surfaces.

Printed patterns have the advantage of being uniform in density. Select designs of distinctive contrast so that different intervals may be readily compared and identified. Not only should patterns vary in design, but they should be of dissimilar tonal value.

COLOR FOR SHADING

Shading sheets also come in a variety of solid colors. These are especially good for original displays, as they are not only attractive, but a color can more quickly be identified and followed than a pattern. If only two or three items are to be defined, tints or shades of the same color may be used.

When a black area is to be shown on a map to be reproduced, use a red shading sheet. The red reproduces black, and the boundary lines to be followed when cutting out the area are easily visible through the color sheet.

WHITE AREAS

When all areas of a shaded map have statistical value, there should be some pattern in each area (see Fig. 9-3). Leaving one area white tends to weaken its importance. Compare maps A and C in Fig. 9-3. The 52 percent area in map A blends too easily into the background.

If, however, the background is black or in tones of gray, the white area will stand out, as in map B.

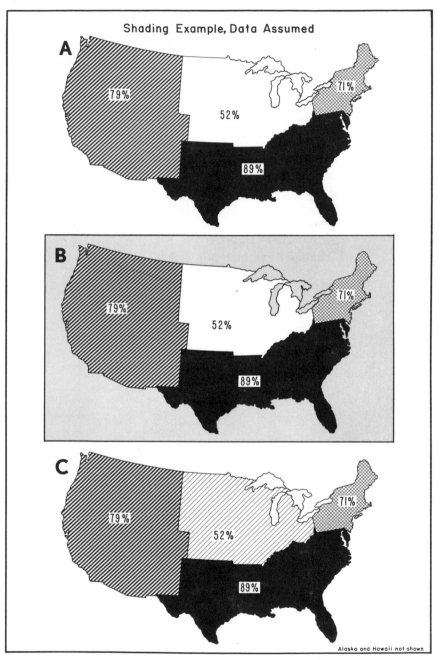

FIG. 9-3   Conquering the white area.

In Fig. 9-4, the primary interest is in the southern portion of the United States. Therefore, value intervals shown on that area are made to stand out more sharply by not shading the rest of the map. At the same time, drawing the whole map locates the states in their proper area.

QUALITATIVE MAPS

Approval or disapproval of a subject and data referring to political preference or military, religious, or economic situations are shown on qualitative shaded maps. Figure 9-5 depicts the status of child labor laws in each state of the United States. Special exemptions are not listed but may be found by referring to the note on the map.

Figure 9-6 shows the food situation in Europe during World War I. Famine conditions and food shortage were serious.

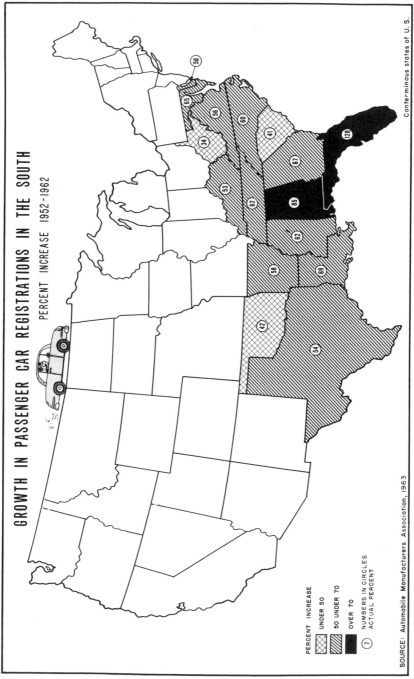

GROWTH IN PASSENGER CAR REGISTRATIONS IN THE SOUTH

PERCENT INCREASE 1952-1962

Conterminous states of U. S.

PERCENT INCREASE

UNDER 50

50 UNDER 70

OVER 70

NUMBERS IN CIRCLES
ACTUAL PERCENT

SOURCE: Automobile Manufacturers Association, 1963

FIG. 9-4 Quantitative regional interest.

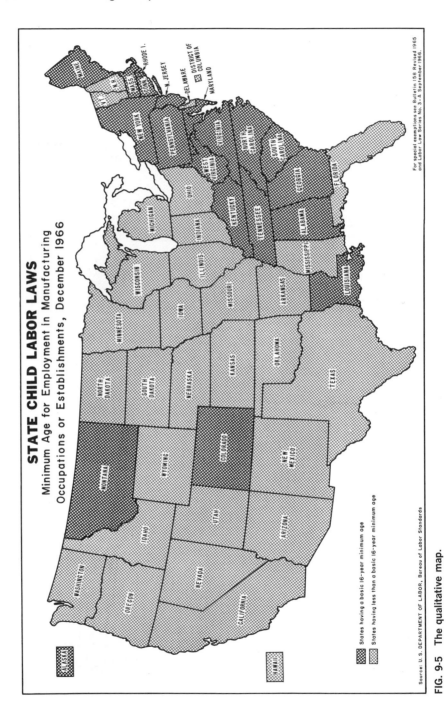

STATE CHILD LABOR LAWS

Minimum Age for Employment in Manufacturing
Occupations or Establishments, December 1966

Source: U. S. DEPARTMENT OF LABOR, Bureau of Labor Standards

For special exemptions see Bulletin 158 Revised 1965
and Labor Law Series No. 3-A September 1966.

☒ States having a basic 16-year minimum age

☒ States having less than a basic 16-year minimum age

FIG. 9-5   The qualitative map.

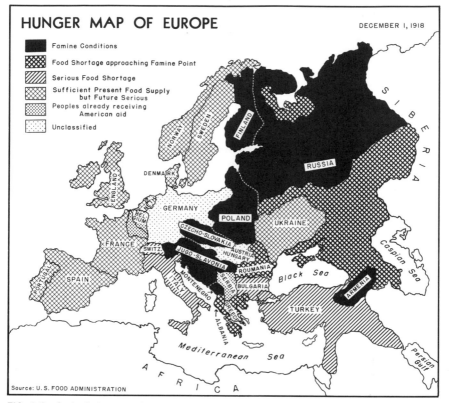

FIG. 9-6 A shaded economic map.

USING TABLES ON MAPS

There will be occasions when the actual data in the form of a table will show to advantage on a map. Figure 9-7 employs this method. The United States is divided into regions, listing the states in each region and their population per square mile. The shading denotes those above or below the United States average.

The figure for the District of Columbia is based on a 61 sq mile land area with 12,442 persons per square mile. St. Louis, Missouri, the tenth-ranking city in size and with the same land area, has 12,255 persons per square mile.

ILLUSTRATIONS ON SHADED MAPS

To make a shaded geographic map more interesting, simple illustrations may be used. Figure 9-8 gives a general picture of the major forest regions and pictures commercially useful trees. The legend lists the more abundant trees in each region.

Figure 9-9 tells a different story. At first glance the layout appears fairly simple. But as you read on, the fractions involving acreage, trees, and population become more or less confusing. It takes at least a second reading to clearly translate the verbal message into a visual picture.

The title "Timber-r-r!," the lumberjack's warning call, is a subtle warning that all may not be clear on the map chart.

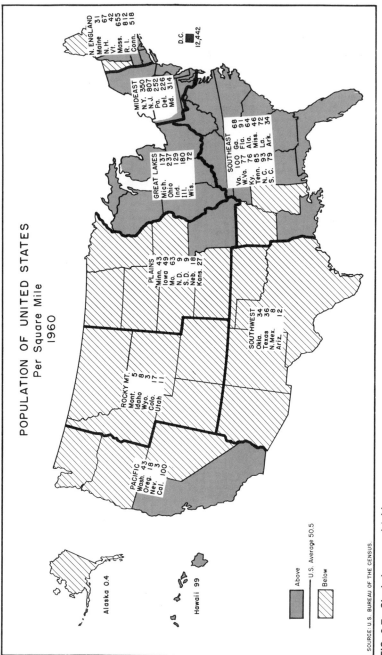

POPULATION OF UNITED STATES
Per Square Mile
1960

N. ENGLAND
Maine   31
N.H.   67
Vt.   42
Mass.   655
R. I.   812
Conn.   518

D.C. 12,442

MIDEAST
N.Y.   350
N.J.   807
Pa.   252
Del.   226
Md.   314

SOUTHEAST
Va.   100
W.Va.   77
Ky.   76
Tenn.   85
N.C.   93
S. C.   79

Ga.   68
Fla.   91
Ala.   64
Miss.   46
La.   72
Ark.   34

GREAT LAKES
Mich.   137
Ohio   237
Ind.   129
Ill.   180
Wis.   72

PLAINS
Minn.   43
Iowa   49
Mo.   63
N.D.   9
S.D.   9
Neb.   18
Kans.   27

SOUTHWEST
Okla.   34
Texas   36
N.Mex.   8
Ariz.   12

ROCKY MT.
Mont.   5
Idaho   8
Wyo.   3
Colo.   17
Utah   11

PACIFIC
Wash.   43
Oreg.   18
Nev.   3
Cal.   100

Alaska 0.4

Hawaii 99

Above
U.S. Average 50.5
Below

SOURCE: U. S. BUREAU OF THE CENSUS.

FIG. 9-7 Shaded map and tables.

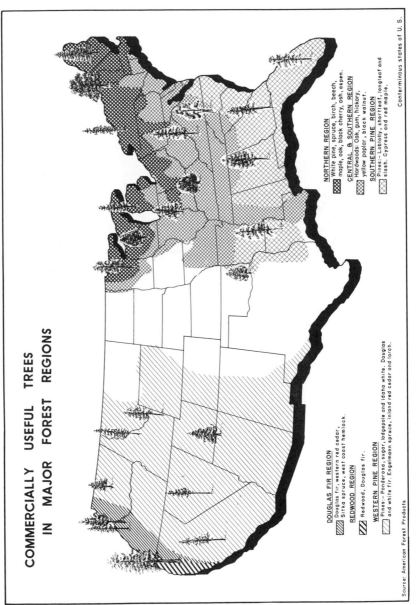

FIG. 9-8   Illustrating the shaded map.

TIMBER ·!·!

¹/₃ OF OUR SAW-TIMBER STAND
IS IN A PART OF
TWO STATES

ANOTHER ¹/₃ SPREADS OVER
³/₄ OF OUR COMMERCIAL FOREST
LAND AREA

BUT less than one-fourth of the original
saw-timber stand remains. More than one-
third of this is in western Oregon and
Washington, while the East with three-
fourths of the land and four-fifths of
the people has less than one-third of
the timber.

FIG. 9-9   Pictorial map and text.

DOT LOCATION

The simplest form of dot map is one in which the dots denote geographic locations. These locations may be of cities where headquarters, branch offices, representatives, or salesmen are located; where natural resources or supplies needed for manufacturing a finished product are found around the world; where refineries, plants, factories are situated; or where any subject is adaptable to a set location.

The dots can be visualized by drawn circles or by pressure-sensitive dots which come in different sizes and colors. Tacks or map pins may be used. These also come in colors; some are coded and have the advantage of being movable when used on a display or working board.

If the surface of the map has a hard finish, pressure-sensitive dots can be removed and replaced in another position without damaging the paper. Figure 9-10 shows how easily they may be applied. The dots, carried on a transparent tape, extend just enough over the edge of the tape so that when positioned a slight pressure will remove them from the tape onto the exact position where needed (see Figs. 9-10 and 9-16B).

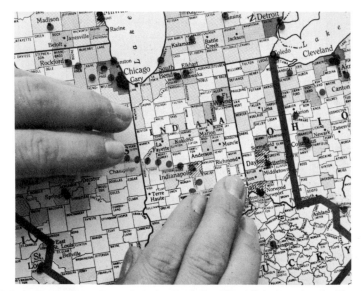

FIG. 9-10   Applying Trans-Pak dot symbols. (Chart-Pak, Inc., Leeds, Mass.)

To enlarge the story on a dot map, pressure-sensitive tapes in colors or patterns can be used to follow routes from place to place. Colored yarns have often been used effectively on pin maps.

Figure 9-11 shows the location of general agents of a life insurance company. Arrows have been used in states having no offices to direct those interested to cities handling their insurance affairs.

DOT DENSITY

In a dot-density map, the dots assume a numerical value. While in Fig. 9-12 the data may not show the exact outline of the cities and towns, it does depict where the population in the counties is concentrated.

The positioning of the data as accurately as possible portrays the density of the geographic distribution of the data, which is the objective of this type of map chart.

Dot-density plotting shows up best when the data are concentrated in small areas, as for locating different crop productions, cattle-raising localities, accidents on freeways or street intersections, or any data of numerical value that is suitable for geographic concentration.

Pressure-sensitive dots are a great time saver in this type of map chart (see Fig. 9-10).

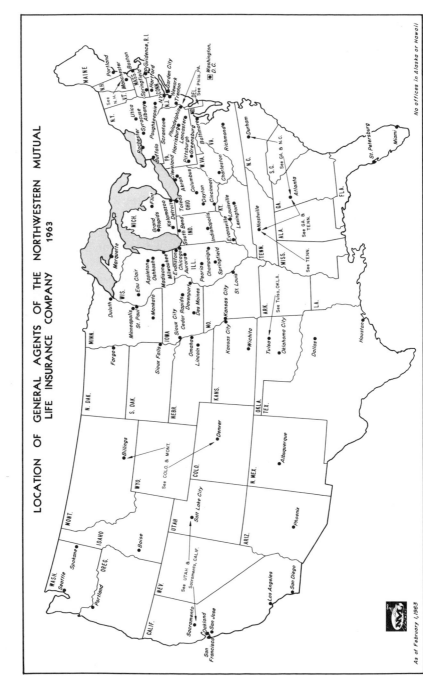

FIG. 9-11 The dot-location map.

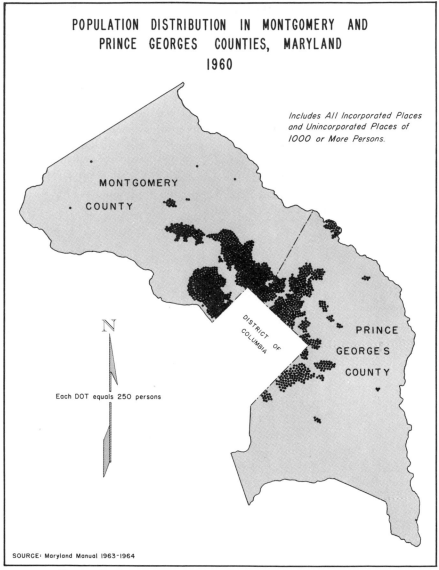

POPULATION DISTRIBUTION IN MONTGOMERY AND
PRINCE GEORGES COUNTIES, MARYLAND
1960

*Includes All Incorporated Places
and Unincorporated Places of
1000 or More Persons.*

MONTGOMERY

COUNTY

DISTRICT OF COLUMBIA

PRINCE
GEORGES
COUNTY

N

Each DOT equals 250 persons

SOURCE: Maryland Manual 1963-1964

FIG. 9-12   The dot-density map.

A SQUARE FOR DENSITY

The map of Washington County, Maryland (see Fig. 9-13), shows the heavy concentration of population in the northeast section of the county. This was due to the steady shift of workers from farm to urban areas, accompanied by the influx of skilled and white-collar workers to industries.

In this map the square symbol was used instead of the more familiar dot-density symbol to depict this concentration. A numerical value was given to each square. While the squares must be counted if the approximate number of persons is to be judged, they are much easier to estimate than the dots, which overlap. This form of layout is a popular-appeal approach to presentation for portraying density of data on a map.

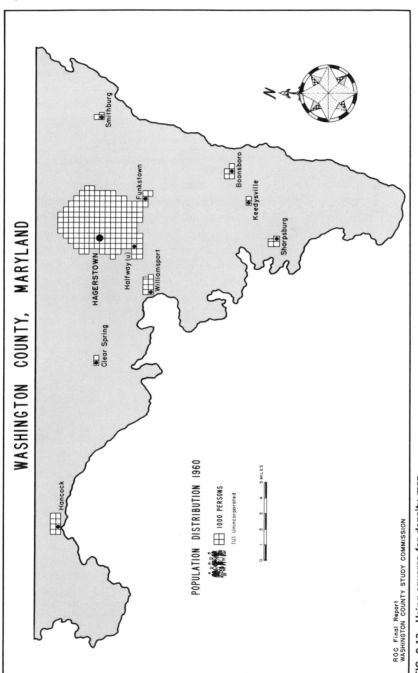

FIG. 9-13 Using squares for density map.

DOTS SYSTEMATICALLY ARRANGED

The dots in Fig. 9-14, representing a numerical value, have been systematically arranged within their relative geographic area. Each dot equals 5 percent. Figures were carried to the next symbol if equal to one-half or over one-half the value of one symbol. That is, 32.1 was plotted as six dots, while 32.7 rated seven dots.

As the actual data are lettered on the map, the dots serve as a visual comparison. District 2 is combined with district 1.

CIRCLES ON MAPS

Circles of different sizes to represent data are not generally used for map charts to be presented for public viewing. While the placing of the circles will give the geographic location of the information, it is difficult to compare their areas. The common error is to make *diameters* proportional to the size of the data instead of the *areas of the circles*. However, if varying circles are used, a diametric scale should be drawn in conjunction with the legend (see Fig. 8-7).

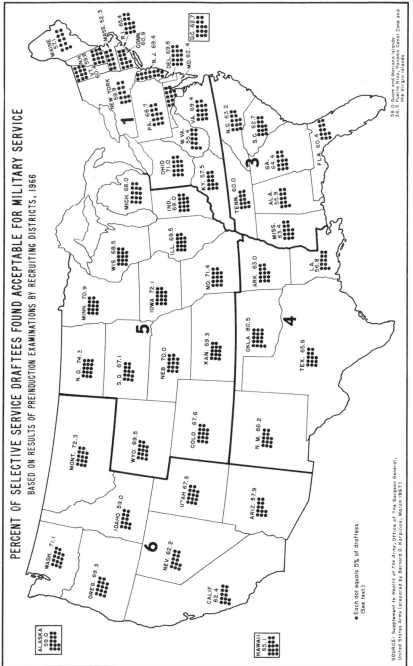

PERCENT OF SELECTIVE SERVICE DRAFTEES FOUND ACCEPTABLE FOR MILITARY SERVICE

BASED ON RESULTS OF PREINDUCTION EXAMINATIONS BY RECRUITING DISTRICTS, 1966

• Each dot equals 5% of draftees.
(See text.)

SOURCE: Supplement to *Health* of *The Army*, Office of The Surgeon General,
United States Army (prepared by Bernard D. Karpinos, March 1967.)

FIG. 9-14 Dots systematically arranged.

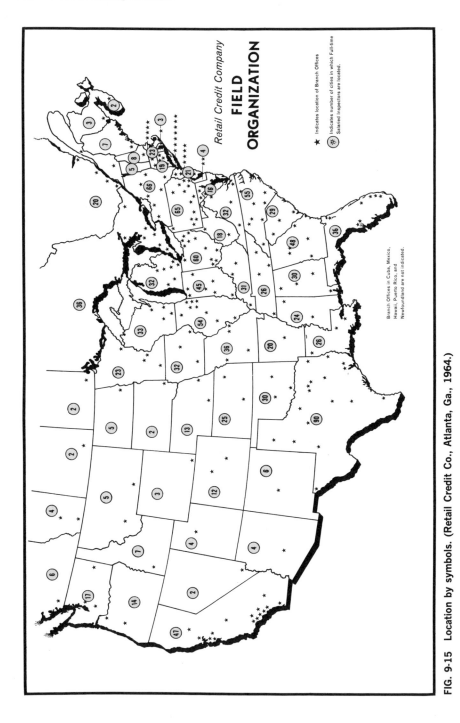

FIG. 9-15   Location by symbols. (Retail Credit Co., Atlanta, Ga., 1964.)

SYMBOLS ON MAPS

Diverse symbols, each representing a variable, are commonly used on maps. Figure 9-15 shows star symbols to locate the number of branch offices of the company. The number in the gray circles indicates the number of cities in each state in which there are full-time salaried inspectors.

The circles and numbers were made by first locating medium gray, pressure-sensitive, Trans-Pak No. 2500, die-cut dots on the map. Over these were centered the circles and numerals of Cello-Tak transfer type, No. 4110 (see Fig. 9-16A). As these simply needed to be *rubbed on*, the task was accomplished in minutes. Figures 9-10 and 9-16B show how Trans-Pak is applied.

The map on electricity in Eastern Nigeria locates with a variety of symbols the progress and plans of that country at a specific time (see Fig. 9-17).

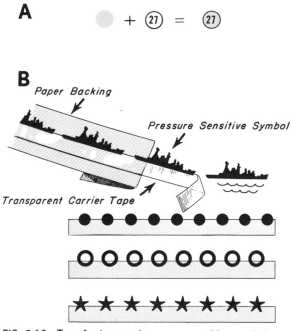

FIG. 9-16   Transfer type and pressure-sensitive symbols.

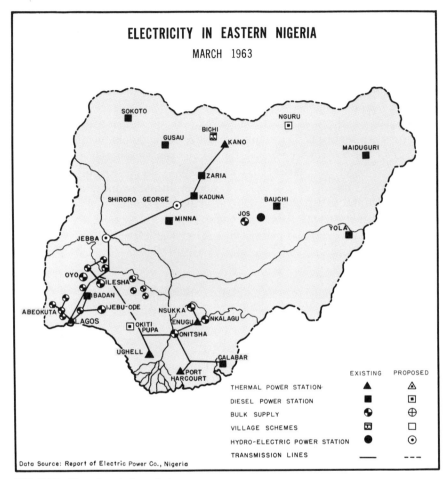

FIG. 9-17   Use of varied symbols.

COLUMNS ON MAPS

Data may be presented in the form of bars, columns, circles, or curves placed geographically on map charts. There has always been the problem of fitting such graphic layouts in the smaller states, as these states seem invariably to have the larger numerical values.

In Fig. 9-18 this is handled by giving the map the appearance of being drawn in perspective. The bases of the columns are so arranged that they rest within the state they represent. The columns are not drawn in perspective, as they would be too difficult

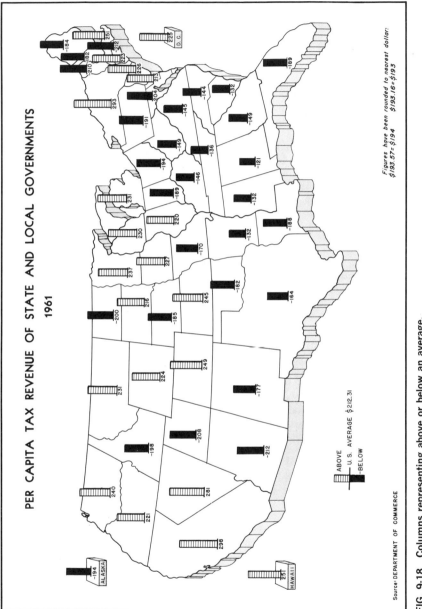

FIG. 9-18 Columns representing above or below an average.

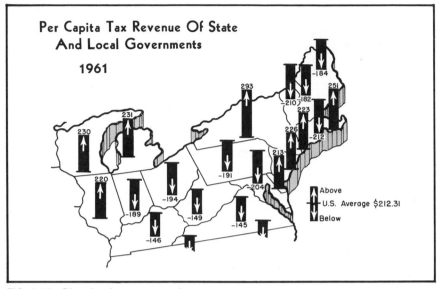

FIG. 9-19   Directional arrows on columns.

to compare, but the slight third-dimensional effect is in accord with the basic map.

The actual amount of tax revenue of state and local governments is noted under each column. The two shadings denote whether the amount is above or below the United States average.

The same data are used for Figs. 9-18 and 9-19. Only a portion of the map is shown in Fig. 9-19, where the deviation data are shown in another manner. Here, the data, whether above or below the average, are noted by directional arrows. The actual numerals are lettered where the arrow points. When the format is a familiar one, a glance at the arrows will show whether the amount is *up* or *down*. The United States average is the base line.

REGIONAL STUDY MAPS

Graphic maps are most essential in research of economic, social, and physical conditions of a community, county, state, or any geographic area to be studied. They are fundamental working media for visually depicting locations of the many factors involved.

Various types of maps can give overall pictures of density of population, prime business districts, community centers, highways, dwelling units, or anything relating to the needs or state of affairs of the area.

The maps in Figs. 9-20 to 9-22 visualize in part a regional study. Assume that a business is looking for an area to open up a branch store. Metro City is being considered, as it is in a section of the country in which the owners would like to locate (see Fig. 9-20A). Map 9-20B shows that the suburban areas are of growing urbanized character with five major trading areas rapidly developing in the regional district (see Fig. 9-21C). These areas are accented on the map by a different shading.

The number of commercial establishments of retail sales and services, and of professional and business firms, represented by grouped columns, were surveyed (see Fig. 9-21D). These businesses could be dot located and coded by type of establishment in separate maps for each trading area.

The sector charts in Fig. 9-22E show the present gross floor area in commercial use, giving an idea of the size of the businesses, while the present employment in these commercial establishments is portrayed on the same chart by pictographs in map F.

Other maps could depict future building and expansion plans in the county, that is, the growth of the trading areas; the accessibility to the proposed locations by routing roads and highway systems; the employment situation; income status; age groups; schools, hospitals, churches, recreation facilities; in fact, all information that would be relative to the new business.

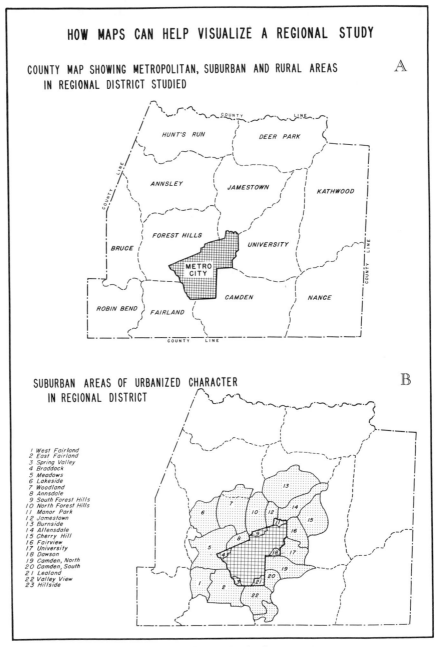

FIG. 9-20 A regional study: metropolitan and suburban areas.

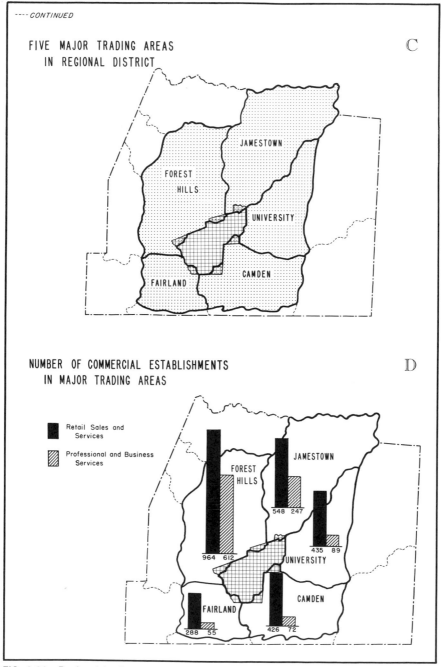

---- CONTINUED

FIVE MAJOR TRADING AREAS
IN REGIONAL DISTRICT   C

NUMBER OF COMMERCIAL ESTABLISHMENTS
IN MAJOR TRADING AREAS   D

FIG. 9-21   Regional trading areas and commercial establishments.

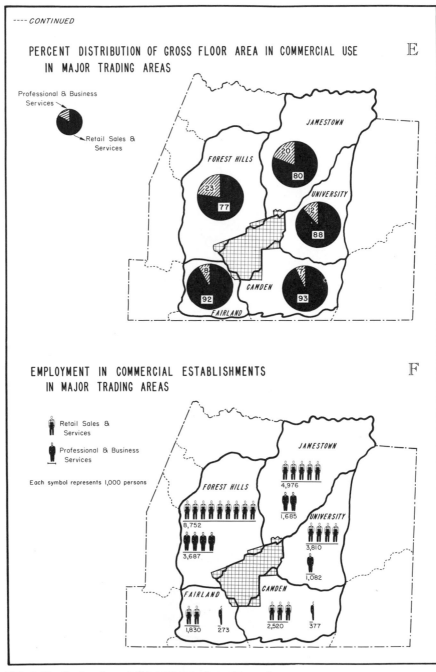

---- CONTINUED

PERCENT DISTRIBUTION OF GROSS FLOOR AREA IN COMMERCIAL USE
IN MAJOR TRADING AREAS   E

EMPLOYMENT IN COMMERCIAL ESTABLISHMENTS   F
IN MAJOR TRADING AREAS

FIG. 9-22 Regional gross floor areas and employment.

REGIONAL BOUNDARIES

When data for the United States pertain to regions and states within those regions, be sure that the regional boundary lines are carefully checked. All offices or businesses do not include the same states within designated regions (see Fig. 9-23).

An attempt was made at one time, in a government department, to standardize the regions on one map for statistical purposes. However the project ended in a confusion of boundary lines when each division of the office justified why a certain state should be within a particular region.

When a region is named in a text, list the states included in that region in a note or reference list. There will then be no doubt about which states are included in the region mentioned.

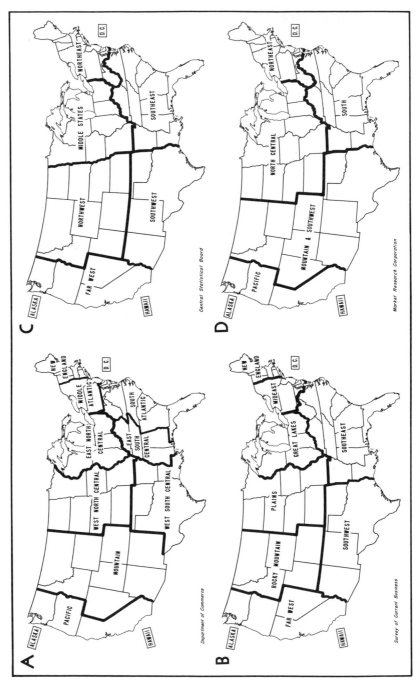

FIG. 9-23 Regional maps vary in their boundaries.

PERSONAL PHOTOS ON MAPS

To give that personal touch to a regional map on a promotive piece, photographs of representatives of the company regional office could be added. Names and phone numbers listed with the photographs would be a quick contact for the prospective client.

Figure 9-24 suggests a layout with the regions outlined and the locations of the representative's office shown.

Call Our Marketing Experts To Help Plan Your Promotion

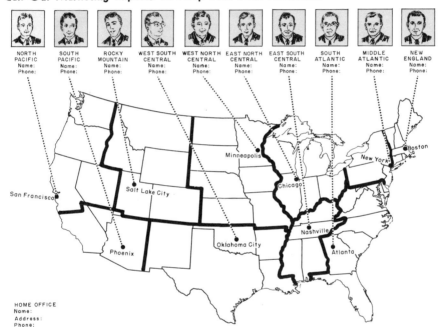

FIG. 9-24 Personalizing a map.

FLOW-LINE MAPS

The flow or route map has many uses. The visual directive layout is far superior to a verbal description. The most popular and familiar flow maps are the standard automobile route or traffic map and those showing shipping and airline routes. Electric systems, transmission lines, oil and gas pipelines, inland waterways, telephone and underground cable layouts all have specific directive flow lines and symbols.

In Fig. 9-25, the flow lines, connecting terminal points, are all the same width. The map dramatically shows how Canada is fast becoming the major supplier of electric power to our nation. It has been found cheaper to buy electric power from Canada than to build the advanced type of power plant required today.

Flow lines may show both quantitative and qualitative data. The width of the lines when depicting such items as imports and exports are usually proportional in width to the numbers they represent. These lines can increase or decrease in width as values are added or subtracted.

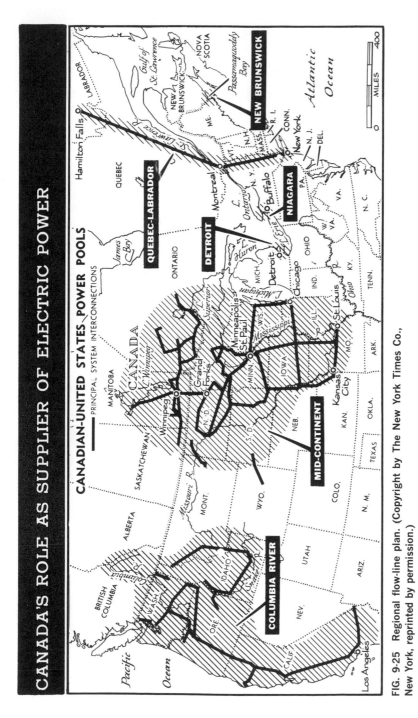

FIG. 9-25   Regional flow-line plan. (Copyright by The New York Times Co., New York, reprinted by permission.)

The flow arrows in Fig. 9-26 portray the source from which minerals are obtained to make razor blades in the United States. Their varying width is artwork.

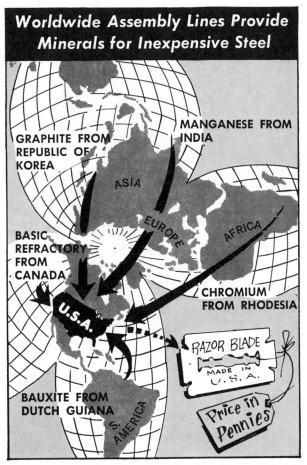

FIG. 9-26   Flow arrows show direction. (American Iron and Steel Institute.)

Arrowheads point the directive movement of hazardous hurricanes in the eastern part of the nation from 1954 to 1964 in Fig. 9-27.

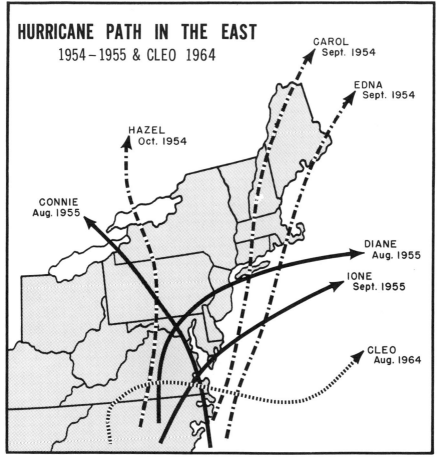

FIG. 9-27 Directive flow-lines.

DISTORTED MAPS

For evaluating data related to land areas, the distorted map will prove useful. In this type of map, the area of each state or country is proportional in size to some actual value other than a physical land-area basis. While this changes the shape of the land area, it gives a general visual impression of the relative importance of the actual value of the area.

A population-proportion map can be helpful in the analysis of business, government activities, or economic conditions. It can serve sales managers, marketing men, management, distributors, economists, politicians, advertisers, and anyone interested in the concentration of their quantitative data in particular areas. The map can be proportioned to total population statistics, selected income classes, age groups, business activities, or other related breakdowns.

MAKING THE DISTORTED MAP

In making and analyzing the distorted map, it must always be kept in mind that the proportional areas represent actual values and not physical areas. While the shape and size of the areas will change, an attempt should be made to maintain their general geographic location.

The maps of the New England states in Fig. 9-28 show by comparison the area differences that result from the use of a map depicting physical land area *A* and the use of one proportioned to an actual value *B*.

The distorted map in Fig. 9-28*B* was originally laid out on cross-section paper, 10 by 10 to the inch. Each square inch equaled 100 sq miles. The number of squares and part squares to be enclosed by the boundary of each state was counted. The land-area shape was kept as near as possible by shifting the count square by square.

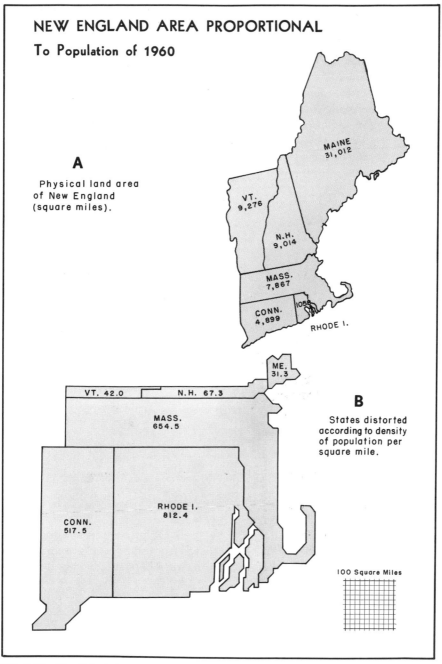

NEW ENGLAND AREA PROPORTIONAL
To Population of 1960

A

Physical land area
of New England
(square miles).

MAINE
31,012

VT.
9,276

N.H.
9,014

MASS.
7,867

CONN.
4,899

1055

RHODE I.

ME.
31.3

VT. 42.0   N.H. 67.3

MASS.
654.5

B

States distorted
according to density
of population per
square mile.

RHODE I.
812.4

CONN.
517.5

100 Square Miles

FIG. 9-28   The distorted map.

This give-a-little, take-a-little process is necessary in the making of a distorted map to keep some semblance of the original land area. It takes trying, fitting, and shifting of squares to retain this shape and at the same time keep its geographic position. But in the end the map's usefulness as a numerical evaluation of the areas is rewarding.

While the square method is not precise, it gives a fair idea of the value area. For more precise measurement of area use a polar planimeter (see Fig. 9-29). With this instrument the area outline may be traced with its pointer and the result read directly in square units from the dial.

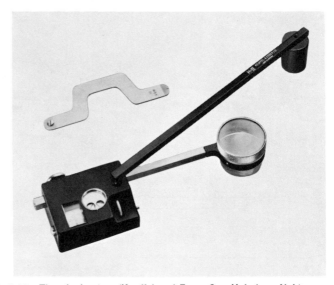

FIG. 9-29 The planimeter. (Keuffel and Esser Co., Hoboken, N.J.)

OUTLINE MAPS

Outline base maps to be used for presenting statistical and economic data may be purchased from stationery, graphic, drafting, map, and lithographic firms or school supply stores.

MAP TRANSPARENCIES

Visiline basic outline map transparencies may be obtained for use on any 10- by 10-in. overhead projector. They cover the hemispheres, countries, or individual states. The transparencies are obtainable as outline maps or as maps showing boundaries, rivers, mountains, or historical outlines.

A transparency consists of one static and one clear acetate overlay, permitting the communicator to mark the overlay indefinitely without damaging the static (see Fig. 9-30).

Do not use a wax-backed shading sheet for transparencies or heat-process printing. The patterns will appear foggy. Obtain pressure-sensitive or overlay sheets of patterns or lettering that will give sharp, ghost-free images for projections, television, or diazo prints.

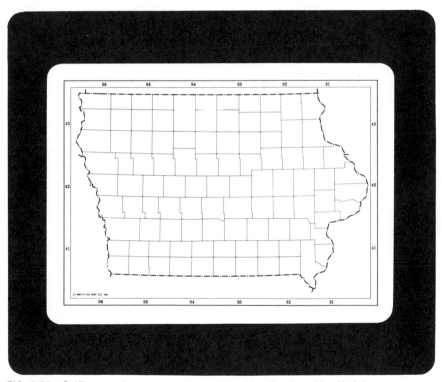

FIG. 9-30   Outline map transparency. (American Map Co., Inc., New York.)

USE OF GLOBES

Globes have always been an attraction, from the small desk model to the large exhibit size.

In the National Geographic Society's headquarters in Washington, D.C., an 11-ft globe dominates the Explorers Hall. The 1,000-lb sphere, driven by electric motors, normally rotates on a spindle, tilted at an angle of 23°27′, as is the plane of the earth's equator (see Fig. 9-31). The spindle, operated by remote control, can be moved in any direction.

FIG. 9-31   The exhibit globe. (Copyright by the National Geographic Society, Washington, D.C.)

Viewers can follow Columbus's historic voyage by watching the projected image of a ship moving across the high seas, or they can see how an outline map of the United States is swallowed up when superimposed on the immense African continent.

Another dimension was added to the rotating globe when a model of the Gemini capsule was used with it. Viewers could follow the path of the orbiting astronauts as if they were standing on the moon (see Fig. 9-32).

Such an exhibit as this could be duplicated by only a few, but the idea of using a globe for displays is feasible. Shipping routes, origins of raw materials, immigration, emigration, and similar data could be followed by using colored or black-and-white patterned tapes. Widths of tape could be scaled to represent certain amounts.

FIG. 9-32 Space model used with globe. (Copyright by the National Geographic Society, Washington, D.C.)

TEN

Pictorial Presentations

PICTORIAL SYMBOLS

The use of pictorial symbols to communicate information is growing universally more popular. When objectively designed, they can supplement or improve the presentation of statistics, economic facts, or social concepts. A visual message not only is retained longer, but is often more expressive than words. It can add greatly to the interest of what otherwise might be a dull subject.

The most essential facts are made clearer when meaningful pictographs are used in annual reports, exhibits, newspaper and magazine articles, and all types of brochures. The chart in Fig. 10-1 follows through with the message by using representative pictorials. Here the symbol has no numerical value, but is used as a lead illustration.

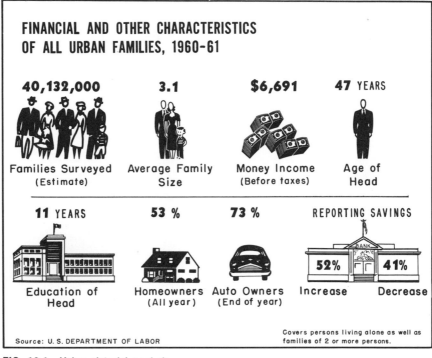

FIG. 10-1   Using pictorial symbols.

DESIGNING PICTOGRAPHS

Should an artist not be at hand for designing pictographs or if local drafting or art supply stores do not carry them, there are commercial firms where they may be bought (see Manufacturers and Suppliers of Visual Presentation Products). However, because of period changes in style, customs, and technology, it is usually more satisfactory to design symbols for a particular need.

During World War I, the United States Food Administration made extensive use of pictorials in their presentation of national and international data for reaching the public. There, under Dr. Raymond Pearl, head of statistics, and Benjamin Louis Padgett, chief of graphics, I first took part in designing and planning charts, maps, brochures, posters, exhibits, models, and other visual materials.

Figures 10-2 and 10-3 depict pictographs designed for use on special occasions.

PICTORIAL SYMBOLS

Scientist   Judge   Grocer

Workman   Policeman   Farmer

Employed   Fireman   Miner

Teacher   Unemployed   Carpenter

FIG. 10-2   Pictographs designed for specific occasions.

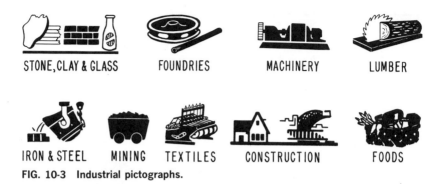

FIG. 10-3 Industrial pictographs.

The pictograph must have a close association with the subject matter so that the reader can comprehend the presentation at a glance. This concept can hold true for a specific audience and for national presentation. However, as dress, habits, and tools are radically different in the nations, the designing of international symbols requires ingenuity and study.

INTERNATIONAL SYMBOLS

Dr. Otto Neurath's *International Picture Language* and *Basic By Isotype* (International System Of Typographic Picture Education, 1936–1937) give an early insight into the advancement in pictorial education. It was his contribution that helped develop picture systems. Contact with Dr. Neurath and Rudolph Modley in the late 1930s and early 1940s further advanced my interest in designing pictographs for government and commercial assignments.

Road signs are the most universally accepted symbols. One in India's Khyber Pass points out roads for vehicles and animals by depicting an automobile or a horse and camel. It does not state, however, what the condition of the vehicle road is.

Figure 10-4 portrays a few symbols representing instruction, information, and warning signs along international highways.

FIG. 10-4   International road symbols.

PICTORIALS AS A UNIT OF MEASURE

When using a symbol in a pictorial bar, treat each symbol as a *unit* of measure.

Part A in Fig. 10-5, comparing number of positions against applicants for those positions, is not clear in its layout. It does not accurately show the *visual* comparison. Part B is correct, as it is laid out in uniform units which visually show there are twice as many applicants as there are positions.

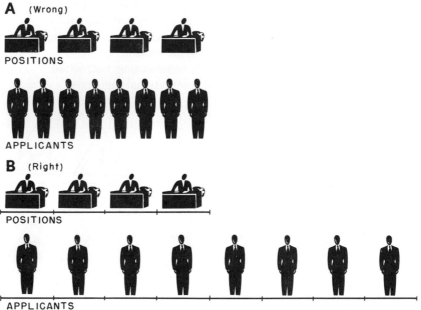

FIG. 10-5   Layout when comparing units of measure.

DIVIDING THE SYMBOL

If data call for part of a symbol, it should be so designed that it is still recognizable when divided. In Fig. 10-6, *A* and *B* can be identified as a house and a man from the portion drawn, but in *C* half a horse representing horsepower keeps the viewer guessing.

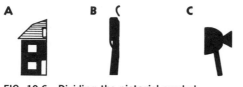

FIG. 10-6   Dividing the pictorial symbol.

Some symbols can be divided into quarters, but it is inadvisable to break them into slivers. The scale in Fig. 10-7 shows how to decide what portion of a symbol should be drawn when the unit measure is 5.

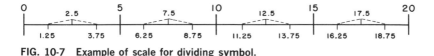

FIG. 10-7   Example of scale for dividing symbol.

Assuming that one-half of a symbol is the smallest unit to be drawn, a number under 1.25 is not depicted; 1.25 and under 3.75 would equal one-half of a symbol; and 3.75 to 5 would call for a whole symbol. This formula follows for the other units; that is, 5.5 would equal one symbol, while 6.9 would be $1\frac{1}{2}$ symbols.

Even when the number of symbols are correctly divided, it is advisable to plot the exact length of the given amount in a line used as a base line for the pictographs. At times, because of the unit of measure, the base line will be *shorter* or *extend beyond* the drawn symbols.

PICTORIAL BAR CHART

The symbols in the chart in Fig. 10-8 are divided into quarters; that is, when 5 is the unit measure, 2.2 is depicted as a one-half symbol, and 3.7 as a three-quarter symbol. The base line serves as a more accurate comparison. (For the use of pictorial bars on maps see Fig. 9-22F.)

Figure 10-9 shows the wrong and right layouts of a pictorial unit bar. Chart A is difficult to read, in that *three* pictographs represent 100,000 persons. This makes it hard to judge what part of a figure represents. When a scale is used, the number of symbols to a unit should be in relation to the scale; that is, in Fig. 10-9 four symbols, each representing 25,000, would equal the unit scale 100,000.

Chart B in Fig. 10-9 uses a systematic unit division with each pictograph equaling 20,000. The actual amount under the varied plotting lines gives a quick and accurate visual reading.

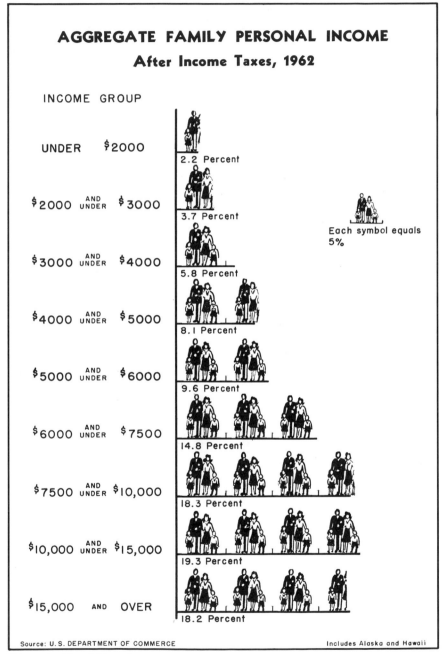

FIG. 10-8   Pictorial bar chart.

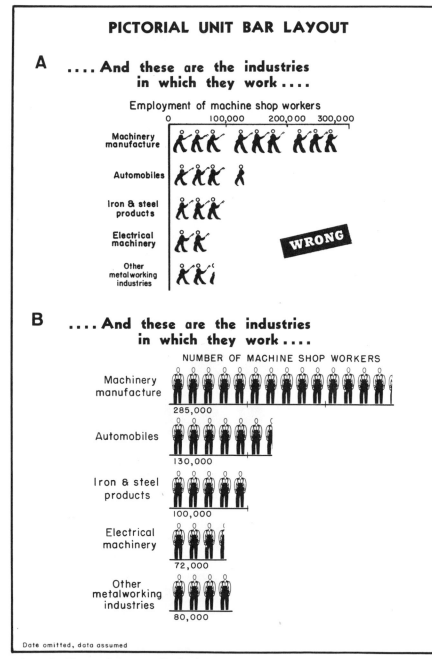

FIG. 10-9   The symbol as a unit of value.

THE SUBDIVIDED PICTORIAL

The most commonly used 100 percent component-bar chart is pictured as a dollar bill. Its components are labeled with legends explaining how the various proportions of the total were used or where they came from.

In Fig. 10-10 the 100 percent is represented by loaves of bread. The components depict the actual amount in cents and the percentages each sharer received from the retail price of a loaf in 1949 and 1965. The percentage figures in italics show that the

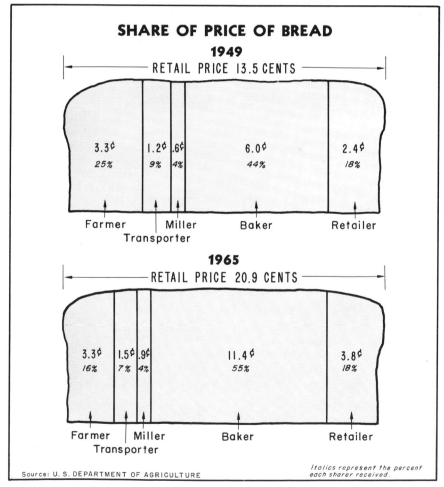

FIG. 10-10   The 100 percent pictorial.

farmer was the biggest loser in his share of the whole, dropping from 25 percent in 1949 to 16 percent in 1965. However, the baker gained, as his share rose from 44 percent in 1949 to 55 percent in 1965.

MORE-OR-LESS PICTORIALS

The poster of hogs shown in Fig. 10-11, can only be termed as a more-or-less picture. It has no recognizable numerical value, and it is impossible to determine the exact amounts. The viewer would see only that more or less was consumed or sent abroad. There is no way to judge whether the pictorials were drawn proportional to the amount as a bar chart or calculated as an area or a volume pictorial. In any case such illustrations should be avoided when statistical values are essential.

FIG. 10-11 "More-or-less" pictorial.

VOLUME PICTORIALS

Volume pictorials drawn in proportion to the value they represent are difficult to compare visually. Height, length, and depth must be considered. For this reason the symbols must be calculated on a volume or three-dimensional basis, even though the pictorial shows only two dimensions (see Fig. 10-12).

To draw a symbol representing 10,000 twice as large as one of 5,000, as in Fig. 10-12A, is erroneous. This actually shows a drawing four times as large in area and eight times as large in volume as the smaller drawing. When a symbol depicts only two dimensions, it is difficult to judge visually whether the size represents area or volume. Figure 10-12B is a correct volume drawing as the dimensions were mathematically found by the following method:

1. Divide the larger number by the smaller number; that is, 10,000 hogs for 1970 divided by 5,000 hogs in 1960 equals 2.

2. The cube root of 2 is 1.26.

3. Apply the cube root to the dimension of the smaller figure.

$$1.26 \times 0.9 = 1.13 \text{ height}$$
$$1.26 \times 1.7 = 2.14 \text{ length}$$

A Incorrect to draw 1970 twice the size of 1960.

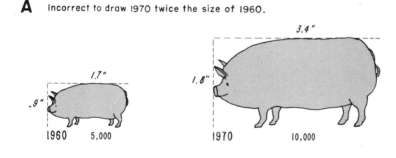

B Correct drawing as third-dimension is considered.

FIG. 10-12   The volume or three-dimensional pictograph.

The third dimension, depth or thickness, is not shown in this type of drawing. But when a symbol represents a three-dimensional picture, it should always be considered in the calculation by the use of the cube root.

Tables for square roots and cube roots may be found in *Standard Mathematical Tables*, Chemical Rubber Publishing Company, Cleveland, Ohio, 1965. They also appear in a paperback edition of the College Outline Series, *Tables for Statisticians*, published by Barnes & Noble, Inc., New York, 1957.

ILLUSTRATIONS

Illustrations on charts employ various media of the graphic arts—pictograms, ink sketches, cutouts, and photographs; many techniques are used, such as airbrush, crayon, watercolor, oil paint, acrylic, and pencil. Each illustration not only must be distinctly related to the subject, but must not be so elaborate as to overbalance the objective of the chart.

The ink drawings in Fig. 10-13 are pertinent to each component of the chart. As food prices vary from year to year, consideration must be given to the availability of the same items and the choice of years to be compared. The items depicted were based on average prices for each commodity, weighted by amounts consumed by an average four-person family. This type of chart could be used as a handout, poster, broadside, or display.

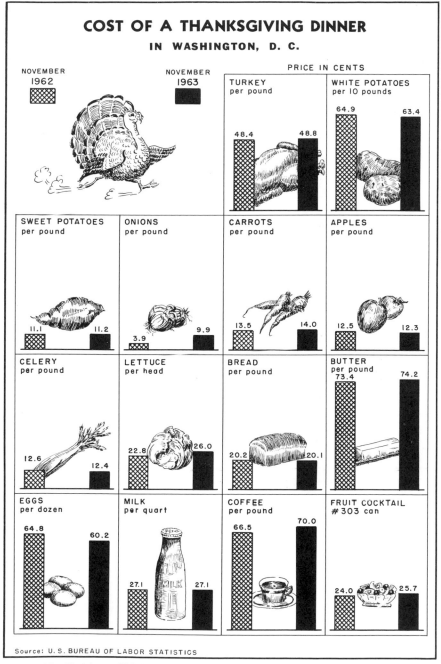

COST OF A THANKSGIVING DINNER

IN WASHINGTON, D. C.

NOVEMBER 1962

NOVEMBER 1963

PRICE IN CENTS

TURKEY per pound — 48.4 / 48.8

WHITE POTATOES per 10 pounds — 64.9 / 63.4

SWEET POTATOES per pound — 11.1 / 11.2

ONIONS per pound — 3.9 / 9.9

CARROTS per pound — 13.5 / 14.0

APPLES per pound — 12.5 / 12.3

CELERY per pound — 12.6 / 12.4

LETTUCE per head — 22.8 / 26.0

BREAD per pound — 20.2 / 20.1

BUTTER per pound — 73.4 / 74.2

EGGS per dozen — 64.8 / 60.2

MILK per quart — 27.1 / 27.1

COFFEE per pound — 66.5 / 70.0

FRUIT COCKTAIL #303 can — 24.0 / 25.7

Source: U.S. BUREAU OF LABOR STATISTICS

FIG. 10-13   Sketches add interest.

Photographs used as a background for a graph can enhance a chart that may otherwise appear too statistical for popular presentation. A white trend line is usually more distinctive on the photograph (see Fig. 10-14).

FIG. 10-14   Photograph used as a pictorial background. (Photo by Albert Spear.)

An airbrush study, as in Fig. 10-15, can be effectively rendered for a message. This type of chart could be used for any kind of company report.

OUR COMPANY'S UNION LABOR GROWTH

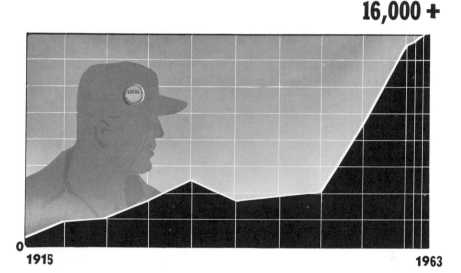

16,000 +

1915   **1963**

800

FIG. 10-15   Use of airbrush for illustrating.

The airbrush is an instrument that sprays a mixture of compressed air and watercolor. It is invaluable in the art department, being used to add toning effects to color or black-and-white art work and lettering; to retouch photography; to spray bromide on any print with a greasy surface; to give a picture background effect, as in Fig. 10-15. In fact, its uses are manifold. The experienced artist will know instinctively how and when to use it.

CHART 3

TOTAL U.S. RETAIL TRADE, MERCHANT WHOLESALERS, SELECTED SERVICES: 1954

Establishments Operated Entire Year by Size of Paid Employment

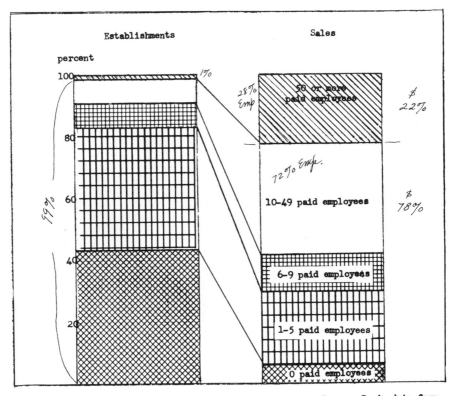

Source: Basic data from
1954 Census of Business
Bulletins R-2-3, W-2-2,
S-2-3

FIG. 10-16   Rough layout used as the basis for Fig. 10-17.

REMAKING CHARTS FOR POPULAR PRESENTATION

For examples of simplifying charts for popular presentation by using pictorials and more readable types of charts, compare Fig. 10-16 with Fig. 10-17 and Fig. 10-18 with Fig. 10-19.

The rough layouts of the components of the 100 percent columns were redrawn into simple pie and bar charts. Pictorials were added to aid in identifying the subject matter.

As the charts were to appear in a booklet depicting the keynotes to the President's Conference on Technical and Distribution Research for the Benefit of Small Business, it was essential that they be readily understood.

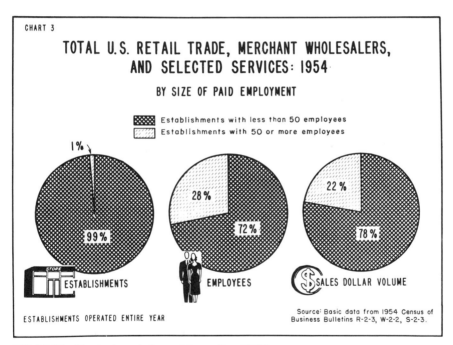

CHART 3

TOTAL U.S. RETAIL TRADE, MERCHANT WHOLESALERS, AND SELECTED SERVICES: 1954

BY SIZE OF PAID EMPLOYMENT

Establishments with less than 50 employees
Establishments with 50 or more employees

1%

28%

22%

99%

72%

78%

ESTABLISHMENTS   EMPLOYEES   SALES DOLLAR VOLUME

ESTABLISHMENTS OPERATED ENTIRE YEAR

Source: Basic data from 1954 Census of Business Bulletins R-2-3, W-2-2, S-2-3.

FIG. 10-17   Pie chart made from data on Fig. 10-16.

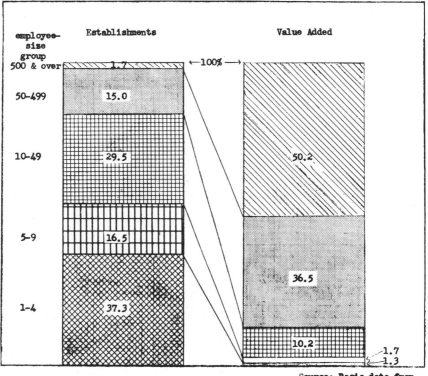

CHART 4

U.S. MANUFACTURING: 1954
Establishments and Value Added *By Manufacturing*
by
Employee-Size Group

Source: Basic data from
1954 Census of Manufactures

FIG. 10-18   Rough layout used as the basis for Fig. 10-19.

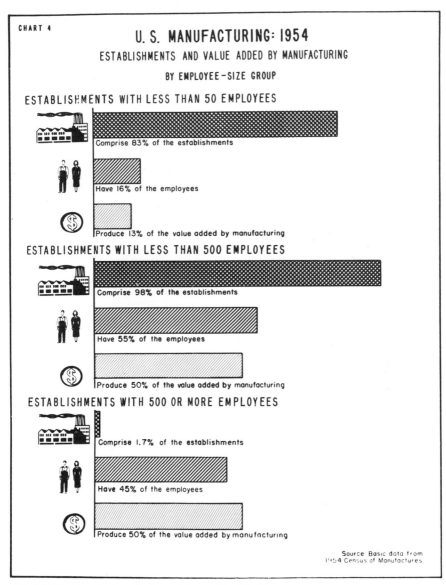

FIG. 10-19   Bar chart made from data on Fig. 10-18.

PICTORIAL DIAGRAMS

Pictographs can point out and stress pertinent points in a subjective book. Figures 10-20 and 10-21, from *The Group Workshop Way in the Church* by Paul F. Douglass, are two pictorial *diagrams* of a series that visually help dramatize how to use the personality sciences of social psychology, group dynamics, cultural anthropology, and science of administration. Figure 10-20 illustrates how integration develops new strengths out of previous divergencies by depicting four methods of settlement and the kind of production resulting from each method.

The pictographs in Fig. 10-21 show group productivity under different types of leadership and the resulting effect of the work performed by each group.

USING CONFLICT CREATIVELY
How Integration Develops New Strengths Out
Of Previous Divergencies

WAYS OF USING CONFLICT

METHOD OF SETTLEMENT

KIND OF PRODUCTION

I. DOMINATION

Victory to one side, defeat to the other; often resent— ment crystalizing into revenge.

2. ARITHMETIC

Decision by the "numbers racket."

3. COMPROMISE

Each one gives up something he values and trades it for something he can accept.

4. CREATIVE INTEGRATION

Discovery of best in all and multiplication of strength from previous divergencies; all come out with more.

MARY E. SPEAR

FIG. 10-20   Pictorial diagram illustrating "Using Conflict Creatively." (From Group Work-shop Way in the Church, by permission of Paul F. Douglass, Association Press, New York.)

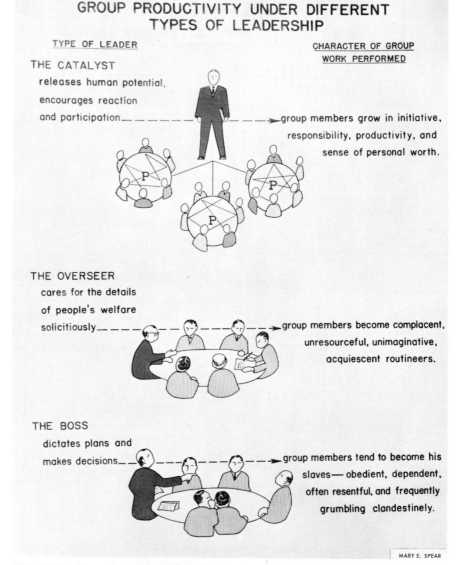

GROUP PRODUCTIVITY UNDER DIFFERENT TYPES OF LEADERSHIP

TYPE OF LEADER

CHARACTER OF GROUP WORK PERFORMED

THE CATALYST
releases human potential,
encourages reaction
and participation _ _ _ _ _ _ _ _ _ _ _ ➤ group members grow in initiative,
responsibility, productivity, and
sense of personal worth.

THE OVERSEER
cares for the details
of people's welfare
solicitiously _ _ _ _ _ _ _ _ _ _ _ ➤ group members become complacent,
unresourceful, unimaginative,
acquiescent routineers.

THE BOSS
dictates plans and
makes decisions _ _ _ _ _ _ _ _ _ _ _ ➤ group members tend to become his
slaves — obedient, dependent,
often resentful, and frequently
grumbling clandestinely.

MARY E. SPEAR

FIG. 10-21 Pictorial diagram outlining "Types of Leadership." (From Group Workshop Way in the Church, by permission of Paul F. Douglass, Association Press, New York.)

PICTORIAL STORY CHART

Figure 10-22 combines a pen-and-brush drawing, simple charts, and pictographs. The story tells the number of migratory laborers who worked, whether their work was farm or nonfarm, and the wages they earned per day. This type of presentation can serve as a broadside, poster, or special report.

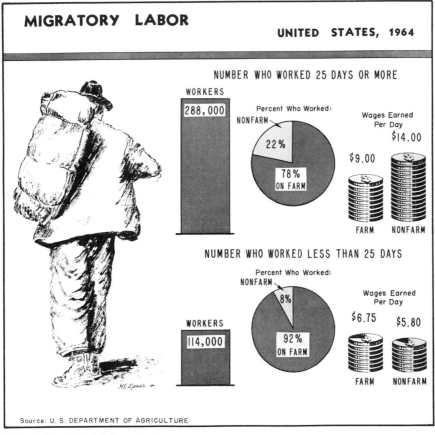

FIG. 10-22   Pictorial story chart.

ILLUSTRATED REPORTS

The pictorial pie chart is one of the most popular presentations used in company or business reports. It is usually portrayed as a silver dollar whose segments show what percent is used for designated items.

The silver-dollar pie in Fig. 10-23 is from a company annual report. The sectors depict their invested assets for the year, while the shaded columns are the policyholder dividends over a five-year period. This is a straightforward presentation with just enough artwork to be pleasing and not confusing.

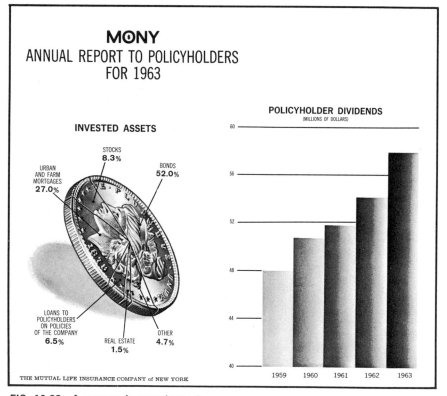

FIG. 10-23   A company's annual report.

Another much used presentation of the silver dollar is the tax dollar. Figure 10-24 shows where the money comes from and where it goes. As a rule the segment divisions start at the twelve-o'clock point, but in this chart the layout is particularly well planned to handle clearly the lettering of the many segments.

MONTGOMERY COUNTY, MARYLAND

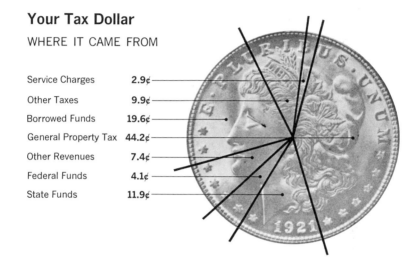

Your Tax Dollar
WHERE IT CAME FROM

Service Charges	2.9¢
Other Taxes	9.9¢
Borrowed Funds	19.6¢
General Property Tax	44.2¢
Other Revenues	7.4¢
Federal Funds	4.1¢
State Funds	11.9¢

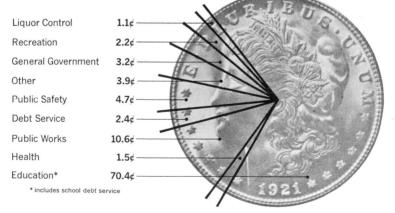

WHERE IT GOES

Liquor Control	1.1¢
Recreation	2.2¢
General Government	3.2¢
Other	3.9¢
Public Safety	4.7¢
Debt Service	2.4¢
Public Works	10.6¢
Health	1.5¢
Education*	70.4¢

* includes school debt service

Source: ANNUAL REPORT 1965

FIG. 10-24   The budget dollar.

In Fig. 10-25, the numerous segments are identified by a number of flags. While the size of the segments can not be compared visually, the actual representative amounts appear on the flags. Being unusual in design, this chart would attract attention to the many functional expenditures of municipal governments.

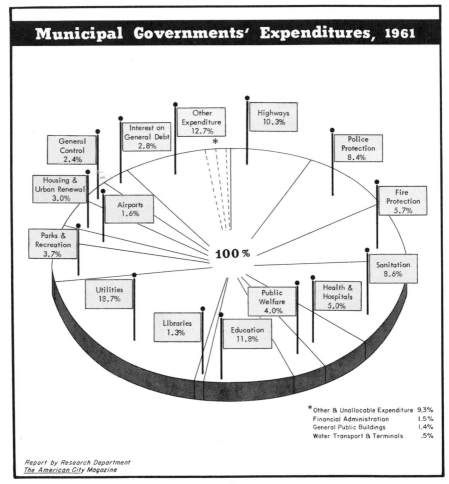

FIG. 10-25 Labeling many sectors in a pie diagram.

CARTOONS

Cartoons depicting charts abound in newspapers, magazines, and various types of publications and displays. Subjectively their humor may strike at politics, current events, situations, or vogues of the times.

The cartoons reproduced here are by the courtesy of Jim Berryman, *The Evening Star*, Washington, D.C. Figure 10-26 appeared during the cigarette-smoking controversy and is still a polemical subject.

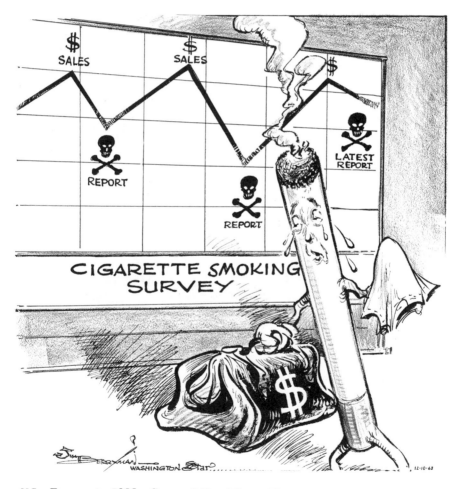

"I Expect I'll Cry All The Way To The Bank!"

FIG. 10-26 The cartoon on a controversial subject.

The cartoon in Fig. 10-27 was printed at the time when prices had registered a slight percentage drop for the month, although they had been steadily rising over a period of two or three years. As with most cartoons, it is necessary to know what event inspired the drawing.

FIG. 10-27   Cartoon on a subject of national interest.

In advertisements the majority of the cartoons are nonstatistical, stressing only the general trends or merits of a product. Figure 10-28, a frame taken from a filmstrip on a consumer survey, compares the upward trend of sales of brand X shirt with the dropping off of brand Y.

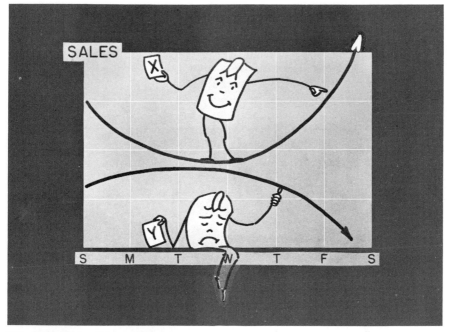

FIG. 10-28   Advertising cartoon.

THE ILLUSTRATED FOLDER

Figure 10-29 suggests ways of using an 8- or 16-panel broadside. Much information can be laid out in this simple form of folder. Panels may be treated individually or spread to suit the charts, data, or information to be presented. In the double fold, a map or company report could be amply displayed on the reverse side.

Check with your printer for the most economical cut of paper for the folder. If it is to be mailed, consider the standard-size envelope you will need.

The folder lends itself to use as a direct-mail advertising piece, in that it can easily adopt the informal tone so necessary to forge a real bond between the advertiser and his reader.

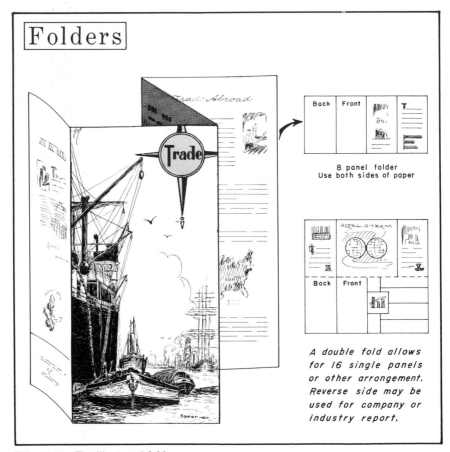

FIG. 10-29   The illustrated folder.

COMPANY PUBLICATIONS

There are few sizable companies that do not publish reports in the form of booklets, house organs, folders, bulletins, etc. The $8\frac{1}{2}$ by 11-in. booklet is the most popular format for public or employee distribution.

This style lends itself to good flexibility in page layout. Length of headlines and text and size of illustrations and tables demand this freedom when one wants a feeling of uniformity of design in text, illustrations, and cover.

Since these publications are to be printed, it is wise to consult with your printer in regard to essentials of the layout. Readability of type must be considered. Avoid using too many type sizes and mixing up type faces. Leave ample but balanced white space on the pages to set off the headings, text, and illustrations. Remember that too much text and too many tables make a dull report for general distribution.

Spare no expense on printing or paper stock. Consider the quality of paper needed for good reproduction of your illustrations. A poor reproduction job is a "lost" report, particularly where color is involved. Try to be original in your layout, but not too visionary.

ELEVEN

Reproduction—Color—
Using Visuals

Each year new or improved methods of reproduction and type-setting are introduced. These improvements may be in installations in large duplicating and printing plants or in small duplicating machines and portable copiers for office use.

When preparing the original visual for reproduction, it must be made on the material suitable for the method selected; that is, the basic material should be transparent, translucent, or opaque. Be sure the artwork and lettering meet the requirements of the process. Paste-ups and overlays may be used on any process that has a negative or plate that can be retouched; other methods must have a clean copy.

The process company which installs the equipment in an office will give full instructions on preparing copy for their method. For reproductions that can not be handled on office equipment, it is advisable to consult a reliable printer. He can recommend not only the best process, but the most economical one.

Whatever method is chosen, consider how the reproduction will be used, the quality required in the finished product, the number of copies needed, and the cost.

Table 11-1 lists the most used reproduction methods. This is followed by a brief comment on each process.

TABLE 11-1   *Selected Reproduction Methods*

Process	Number of copies feasible	Size of original	Size of reproduced page
Photostat	1–15	Up to 29 × 37¾ in.	Up to 18 × 24 in.
Ozalid	1–25	Any length and up to 54 in. wide	Same as original
Offset (Multilith)			
a. Direct-image	26–5,000	Up to 11½ × 14 in.	Same as original
b. Photographic-image	500–25,000	Up to 30 × 40 in.	Up to 17 × 21 in.
Letterpress	Indefinite	Any enlargement or reduction	
Lithography	Indefinite	Any enlargement or reduction	
Gravure	Indefinite	Any enlargement or reduction	
Silk screen	Indefinite	Same as original	
Xerox #2400	Indefinite	8½ × 14 in.	Same as original

THE PHOTOSTAT

When a limited number of copies are needed, the photostat copy may serve the purpose. The photographic negative is a *readable* negative, as it is not reversed.

A most effective exhibit of charts was quickly made for a statistical conference by reproducing photostat negatives of charts on file. The resulting white line trends were lightly rubbed with a kneaded eraser. This removed the chemical solution from the paper and allowed the use of watercolors on the curves. Transparent adhesive color sheets were cut out and used to give color to the bars and columns.

The result was a striking exhibit with white lettering and grids and bright colors against the black background.

OZALID

Ozalid is a whiteprint or diazo process. It makes the same size copies as the translucent originals. A positive reproduction is made directly from a positive. By using different sensitized materials, prints can be made on white paper, film, or cloth. To duplicate a photograph, a positive print must first be made on film instead of paper.

OFFSET (MULTILITH)

In offset printing the inked surface of the plate does not print directly onto the paper, but prints onto a rubber-covered cylinder instead. The image is *offset* from this cylinder onto the paper.

AUDITORIUM ENTRANCE ~ DEPARTMENT of LABOR

FIG. 11-1   Pen-and-ink sketch duplicated by multilith.

The Multilith is a small-size offset printing press that can be used in the duplicating section of an office. It will reproduce typed, lettered, drawn, ruled, or printed matter on duplicating masters from which the press duplicates copies. Figure 11-1 is a pen-and-ink drawing duplicated by Multilith on an office press. The fine pen-and-ink lines appear heavier than in the original drawing.

When making photographic masters, large solid areas of ink as required on bar, column, or surface charts should be avoided, as the inking mechanism cannot handle a large flow of ink. It is better in this situation to use distinctive shading patterns for areas.

LITHOGRAPHY

Lithography (photo-offset) is employed when annual reports, booklets, brochures, and broadsides are predominantly illustrated. But when the material contains mostly text that requires type-setting it is best to use the letterpress process. Offset tends to be cheaper than other processes when a large number of copies, containing many line drawings, must be run.

Lithography is excellent for wash drawings, soft pencil work, and soft color effects. It can handle illustrations that are larger than book and magazine size. However, if posters or signs are to be made on cardboard, the silk screen process must be used.

LETTERPRESS

The letterpress process operates on the relief principle. Raised surfaces are inked and then pressed against the paper. This process gives sharper, cleaner reproduction of type than any other process. It is used for practically all newspapers and books or wherever type must be set.

Letterpress is excellent for reproducing photographs and is almost always preferred when printing on glossy paper. However, if the run is small, photography is cheaper.

The length of the run, the quality of reproduction wanted, and the cost will most often govern the process used.

SILK SCREEN

Silk-screen printing is one of the most versatile printing processes, as it can print on almost any material, such as glass, felt, acetates, metal, wood, paper, and leather. This process is employed not just for "flat" materials, but for souvenir or advertising pieces such as keys, bottles, rulers, pocketbooks, compacts, models, and like objects.

In the process a stencil is cut and placed on the silk which has been tightly stretched on a frame. The paint is applied evenly by means of a squeegee. This forces the paint through the stencil openings in the silk screen and onto the paper or object positioned under the screen.

GRAVURE (ROTOGRAVURE)

The gravure printing process lends itself to high-quality reproduction of photographs and halftones in black-and-white and color.

However, the reproduction of type is not very good, as the process uses a cross-line screen, which tends to make the edges of the letters fuzzy.

XEROGRAPHY (XEROX)

Xerox machines come in various sizes to handle different needs. The No. 2400 machine prints 40 positive copies a minute on ordinary paper. Shading sheets, acetate overlays, and adhesive and rub-on lettering may be used on original artwork. As it is a dry, direct-positive process, the copies may be used immediately.

FILM ON PRINTING PROCESSES

The Printing Industry of Washington, Washington, D.C., has an excellent film available on printing processes. The film, *Basic Reproduction Processes in the Graphic Arts*, covers the fundamentals of the printing industry, including processes, plate production, typesetting, and presses. Produced under the direction of the Visual Arts Committee of the Education Council of the Graphic Arts Industry, the film is a 16-mm sound motion picture in color, with a running time of 25 min. It introduces and describes the four basic printing processes—lithography, letterpress, gravure, and silk screen—and explains printing plates from linoleum blocks, to rubber plates, to process cameras. It also covers type production methods, from handset to Linotype and phototype, and printing presses, including platen, rotary, and web types. Common printing surfaces, such as paper, metal, plastic, glass, and cellophane are also discussed in the film.

COLOR OF INK AND PAPER

Be careful in your selection of colors when using a colored ink on colored paper or board stock. Select not only the colors wanted but the *tone* of the colors. A series of charts was printed on a deep blue paper with black lettering and line work. The information was practically unreadable.

The following combinations of colors are listed in their order of legibility. However, in selecting a combination, think of the nature of your visual and your audience. Be sure the colors are suitable for the occasion.

1. Black on yellow paper
2. Green on white paper
3. Blue on white paper
4. White on blue paper
5. Black on white paper
6. Yellow on black paper
7. White on red paper
8. White on orange paper
9. White on black paper
10. Red on yellow paper
11. Green on red paper
12. Red on green paper

PRINTING INK COLOR GUIDES

Bourges Color Corporation has a visual color system of standardized printing ink colors. It shows 60 transparent sheets matched to printing ink standards that have been set up by the graphic arts industry to simplify the problems of color matching for all forms of commercial printing.

International Printing Ink (IPI), a division of Inter-chemical Corporation, has a pocket color guide of 108 colored inks. The IPI guide was printed under normal pressroom conditions. IPI also has a special specimen book showing 23 of the most popular colors and 6 selected blacks. I find the guide most helpful in selecting inks for white cover stock.

COLOR IN VISUALS

Presentations, to be striking, should be reduced to a few color combinations and restrained in the *steps* of value. Value is concerned with distinguishing the gradations of light colors (tints) from dark colors (shades), as navy blue from sky blue or flesh pink from rubine red. Color in the visuals can be affected by the illumination and immediate surroundings where they are displayed. Consider this in your planning and selection of color schemes.

In making decisions, remember that:

1. Dark colors absorb light and make areas seem smaller.

2. Light colors reflect light and make areas appear larger and further away.

3. Bright colors attract the eye, but use them cautiously when in juxtaposition, as they can be distracting.

4. Warm colors, such as reds, oranges, yellows, and yellow-greens, are stimulating and seem to advance toward you.

5. Cool colors, such as blues, blue-greens, and violets, are subduing and appear to recede.

COLOR BLINDNESS

In using color, the chance of color blindness must at times be considered. The most common type of color blindness is that of not being able to distinguish between red and green. If this problem seems important for some special occasion, use a deep chrome yellow and dark cobalt blue on a light gray background. The colors will not only be distinguished at a distance but be pleasing to the eye.

Avoid using very deep or dark colors, as it is difficult to tell them apart, even at a short distance.

USING THE VISUALS

When it comes time to put on the big show, be certain that your different media are coordinated. Your charts, your projections, your exhibit, and your handouts should each be planned to serve its own purpose, but each must be closely related to the other. There must be no question about your primary objective.

Prior to the meeting:

1. *Check the arrangement and display of both the visuals and the duplicated materials.*

2. *Set all props in order.* Any extra tables, easels, pointers, or accessories needed for special effects should be easily within reach.

3. *Be familiar with the microphone.* If possible try it out before the meeting. The more familiar you are with it, the more at ease you will be when speaking.

An embarrassing experience occurred at a meeting I attended, when the clasp on the cord of the microphone broke and it couldn't be fastened around the speaker's neck. A clip microphone was hastily given him, but the speaker wore a modern suit with no pocket or lapel to fasten it to. No mike stand was available, so when he had to handle his material, the microphone had to be laid down.

PRESENTATIONS WITH CHARTS

You are, of course, familiar with your story. But be so familiar with it that light notes written on the charts or a brief reference outline will carry you on with your subject. In this way you will avoid having to read a written speech, which most often makes an audience restless.

1. *Keep each chart covered until you are ready to introduce it.*

2. *Use two easels when comparing one chart with another.*

3. *Give an element of surprise to the talk.* Cover part of the chart with a flap and lift it at the right moment.

4. *Don't read the title.* The audience can do that. Make your point about the chart, telling definitely what it shows.

5. *Encourage the audience to make notes of anything they question or would like to know about.* This usually promotes a more attentive audience and a livelier follow-up period.

PRESENTATIONS WITH PROJECTIONS

It is an exceptional showing that has no "bugs" in it. So when possible make all necessary preparations beforehand.

When presentation is to be projected:

1. *Know where the light switches are.* Someone on hand should be familiar with their locations; otherwise lights will be popping on and off. This may be amusing to the audience, but is distracting to the speaker.

2. *Have the projector in the right position for the screen.* Improper positioning of equipment can cause another delay, while the operator tries to find the right focus.

3. *Check the slides or transparencies.* See that they are all in order with the right side up. If this is not done, further confusion and delay may result.

4. *Leave some light on in the room.* Ample light should be on so your audience can see to take notes. Be happy that they think enough of your talk *to take* notes.

5. *Show each visual only long enough to register.* One visual may become confused with your next subject, if left in focus too long.

EXHIBIT PANELS AND KITS

Exhibits are the basic visual display at conventions and conferences. After your presentation, should you have an exhibit of your topic, be sure to give full directions about where to find it. Figure 11-2 shows a simple arrangement, with well-prepared charts. The table provides a place for handouts and cards for taking names and addresses. The seating arrangement is especially inviting. If you have been to many conventions, you well understand how welcome it is to have a place to sit down. This particularly helps to make one feel welcome.

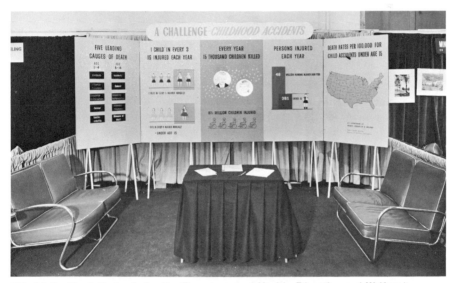

FIG. 11-2   Chart display in booth. (Department of Health, Education and Welfare.)

If you do not have a booth, Fig. 11-3 shows a good arrangement for an entrance or hallway. Reproductions used in your speech or other materials can be handed out or placed on tables for the audience to see when it leaves the auditorium.

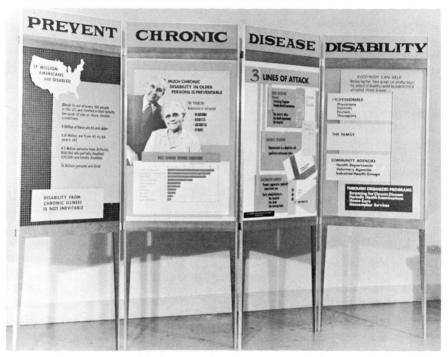

FIG. 11-3 Panel display. (U.S. Department of Health, Education and Welfare.)

Figure 11-4 shows folding panels of versatile use. These are obtainable in five different panel surfaces and can double as room dividers. They provide 144 sq ft of exhibit space and fold at any angle. An exhibit can be wired with Satellight exhibit lamps should you be in an otherwise unlighted area.

FIG. 11-4 SHOWPLACE panels with Satellight exhibit lamps. (The Brewster Corporation, Old Lyme, Conn.)

The featherweight, colorful panels shown in Fig. 11-5 are part of a do-it-yourself exhibit kit. In only a few minutes you can assemble it by locking the panels with a device called Panelock. A closeup is shown in the photograph. This kit packs away into a 25- by 25- by 4-in. hand-luggage carrying case and weighs only 21 lb.

FIG. 11-5 Table exhibit panels held with plastic Panelocks. (William Hayett, Inc., New York.)

Another kit of the same light weight is particularly good for trade shows and professional meetings. Three units will fill a 10-ft exhibit booth. It has an ample display space, a storage compartment, and a sturdy ledge or browsing counter which can support a substantial weight. Figure 11-6 shows the completed structure framed in aluminum. Accessories included in the kit are lettering, hanging devices, an electric flasher, and an awl for punching holes precisely sized for pegboard fittings.

FIG. 11-6   A complete portable display kit. (William Hayett, Inc., New York.)

The portable exhibit display board shown in Fig. 11-7 is pegboard trimmed in aluminum. Assembly requires only joining together the two large panels, hooking on the two wings, and affixing the header atop the assembled unit. Constructed of plated steel tubing, each leg is fitted with a nonscuff plastic glider. The kit is equipped with a selection of 50 pieces of pegboard hardware for mounting display material. This sturdy unit can be exhibited in any location where your message will be seen by the largest possible audience.

There are of course a great variety of exhibits built with mechanical devices and using models. These are always eye-catchers. The main thing is to make the most of what you have.

Just remember that the visual image that tells its story in a forceful way will be remembered longer. Simplicity is the first rule in any presentation.

FIG. 11-7 A portable kit that serves as a showcase. (Porta-Zibit, Washington, D.C.)

Bibliography

GRAPHIC PRESENTATION AND STATISTICS

ALLEN, E. S.: "Six Place Tables," McGraw-Hill Book Company, New York, 1947. Most frequently used tables with explanation and instruction.

BRINTON, W. C.: "Graphic Presentation," Brinton Associates, New York, 1939. Profusely illustrated with charts, maps, and diagrams from various sources. Each has a comprehensive comment.

CLARK, W.: "The Gantt Chart," Pitman Publishing Corporation, New York, 1952. Depicts how this simplified time chart can be adjusted to an individual business.

Committee on Standards for Graphic Presentation: "Time Series Charts, A Manual of Design and Construction," American Society of Mechanical Engineers, New York, 1938. Basic principles in the design and layout of statistical charts.

FUNKHOUSER, H. G.: "Historical Development of the Graphical Representation of Statistical Data," The Saint Catherine Press, Ltd., Bruges, Belgium, 1937 (reprinted from *Osiris*, vol. 3, part 1). Accounts of the earliest charts made by William Playfair, whose first known book was published in London in 1786.

HAEMER, K. W.: "Making the Most of Charts," American Telephone Company, New York, 1960 (booklet). Discusses the less technical aspects of graphic presentation.

HANSON, K. O.: "Managerial Statistics," Prentice-Hall, Inc., New York, 1955. Practical data and methods useful to management in planning and controlling organizational activities.

HUFF, D.: "How to Lie with Statistics," W. W. Norton & Company Inc., New York, 1954. Tells why graphs may not always be what they seem.

MILLER, R. W.: "Schedule, Cost, and Profit Control with PERT," McGraw-Hill Book Company, New York, 1963. A comprehensive appraisal of PERT (Program Evaluation and Review Technique) management systems; how PERT methods can be used in commercial, industrial, and economic planning and control activities.

MODLEY, R.: "How to Use Pictorial Statistics," Harper & Brothers, New York, 1937. Shows how the pictograph serves as an essential tool for communication.

NEURATH, O.: "International Picture Language," Kegan Paul, Trench, Trubner & Company, Ltd., London, 1936.

————: "Basic by Isotype," Kegan Paul, Trench, Trubner & Company, Ltd., London, 1937. Both books are on the development of a system of international picture language. The pictographs symbolize Basic English words.

PEDRONI, FERNANDO: "Rappresentazioni Statistiche," Casa Editrico Ulrico Hoepli, Milan, Italy, 1968. A practical book for the study of statistical, demographical, and actuarial sciences presentation.

RIGGLEMAN, J. R., and I. N. FRISBEE: "Business Statistics," McGraw-Hill Book Company, New York, 1951. Emphasizes the practical application of statistics to business problems.

SPEAR, M. E.: "Charting Statistics," McGraw-Hill Book Company, New York, 1952. Describes types of charts and basic rules for their use.

WHITE, K. K.: "Understanding the Company Organization Chart," American Management Association, New York, 1963. Examines all forces important in the shaping of the company's structure. Shows growth or retrogression, shifts formal and informal relationships, and cites case histories as examples.

GRAPHIC ARTS

BUSTANOBY, J. H.: "Principles of Color and Color Mixing," McGraw-Hill Book Company, 1947. Color systems, values, legibility at a distance, and definitions of color terms.

CARLYLE, P., G. ORING, and H. S. RICHLAND: "Learning to Letter," McGraw-Hill Book Company, New York, 1939. Use of Speedball pens and brushes, styles of lettering and their variations.

MAURELLO, S. R.: "Commercial Art Techniques," Tudor Publishing Company, New York, 1952. Covers various fields of illustration, tools, working methods, layout, lettering, and production.

MELCHER, D., and N. LARRICK: "Printing and Promotion Handbook," McGraw-Hill Book Company, 1966. Handbook on problems in use, production, and purchase of materials for promotion and advertising.

MUSACCHIA, J. B., H. A. Fluchere, and M. J. GRAINGER: "Airbrush Techniques for Commercial Art," Reinhold Publishing Corporation, New York, 1953. Fundamental principles of airbrushing and their application to art production problems.

ROBINSON, A. H.: "Elements of Cartography," John Wiley & Sons, New York, 1953. Art and science of cartography, drafting equipment and materials, statistical map representation.

SPEAR, J. H.: "Creating Visuals for TV," Division of Audiovisual Instructional Service, National Education Association, Washington, D.C., 1962. Effects shown through the manipulation of cameras and studio techniques can be used to advantage in presenting visuals in still, live, or animated form.

STERNBERG, S.: "Silk Screen Color Painting," McGraw-Hill Book Company, New York, 1942. Pictorial instructions clearly show construction of printing frame and each step for making the print.

STRAUSS, V.: "Point of Purchase Cardboard Displays," Presentation Press, New York, 1954. Simplified construction of display units, motion, lighting, and printing methods.

"Use and Care of Drawing Instruments," Eugene Dietzgen Company, Chicago, Ill. (booklet).

PERIODICALS

Communication Arts, Palo Alto, Calif. 94303.

Industrial Art Methods, Syndicate Magazines, Inc., New York, N.Y. 10036.

Visual Communications Instructor, Syndicate Magazines, Inc., New York, N.Y. 10036.

Manufacturers and Suppliers of Visual Presentation Products

Those interested in visual presentations should make a point of attending educational or trade shows where manufacturers and dealers display their audiovisual equipment and materials. The use of these products is readily demonstrated. Literature or catalogues may be obtained from the following firms.

ART AND DRAFTING SUPPLIES

ACS Tapes, Inc.
Tapes, accessories, pictographs
480 Neponset St.
Canton, Mass. 02021

Alvin & Company, Inc.
Drafting products
611 Palisado Ave.
Windsor, Conn. 06095

American Map Company, Inc.
3 W. 61st St.
New York, N.Y. 10023

Artype, Inc.
Alphabets and patterns°
345 E. Terra Cotta Ave.
Crystal Lake, Ill. 60014

Bee Paper Company, Inc.
Art paper products
100 Eighth St.
Passaic, N.J. 07056

Bourges Color Corp.
Color screens, acetates, paints
80 Fifth Ave.
New York, N.Y. 10011

°The *patterns* supplied by firms in this list include shading media, numbers, symbols, arrows, rules, borders, and ornaments.

Milton Bradley Company
Art and drafting
74 Park St.
Springfield, Mass. 01101

Robert J. Brady Company
Audiovisual training materials
130 Q St., N.E.
Washington, D.C. 20002

Arthur Brown & Bro., Inc.
Art and drafting
2 W. 46th St.
New York, N.Y. 10036

The Carter's Ink Company
239 First St.
Cambridge, Mass. 02142

Cello-Tak
Alphabets, patterns, pictographs,
color film
35 Alabama Ave.
Island Park
Long Island, N.Y. 11558

Chart-Pak, Inc.
Materials for graphic techniques
One River Road
Leeds, Mass. 01053

Codex Book Company, Inc.
Graphic chart papers
74 Broadway
Norwood, Mass. 02062

Craftint Manufacturing Company
Art and drafting
18501 Euclid Ave.
Cleveland, Ohio 44112

Crescent Cardboard Company
Papers and boards
2040 N. Homan Ave.
Chicago, Ill. 60651

The Datak Corp.
Instant lettering
85 Highland Ave.
Passaic, N.J. 07055

Davidson Corp.
Protype, photocomposition
29 Ryerson St.
Brooklyn, N.Y. 11205

Delta Brush Mfg. Corp.
120 S. Columbus Ave.
Mt. Vernon, N.Y. 10553

Eugene Dietzgen Company
Art and drafting
2425 N. Sheffield Ave.
Chicago, Ill. 60614

Duchart, Inc.
Manual for Instant Chartmaking
One West Ave.
Larchmont, N.Y. 10538

A. W. Faber-Castell-Higgins Co.,
Inc.
Art and drafting pencils, inks
41 Dickerson St.
Newark, N.J. 07103

Eberhard Faber
Drawing supplies
P. O. Box 760
Wilkes-Barre, Pa. 18703

Fototype, Inc.
Stack lettering
1414 Roscoe St.
Chicago, Ill. 60657

W. E. French
Drafting supplies
Adams and 3rd Sts.
Hoboken, N.J. 07030

Graphic Products Corp.
Formatt alphabets, patterns
3810 Industrial Blvd.
Rolling Meadows, Ill. 60008

M. Grumbacher, Inc.
Art supplies
460 W. 34th St.
New York, N.Y. 10001

The Holes-Webway Company
Cutout alphabets
St. Cloud, Minn. 56301

Hunt Manufacturing Company
Pens, markers, Speedball
1405 Locust St.
Philadelphia, Pa. 19102

Keuffel & Esser Company
Leroy instruments
30 Speedwell Ave.
Morristown, N.J. 07960

Koh-I-Noor, Inc.
Drawing instruments and
   supplies
100 North St.
Bloomsbury, N.J. 08804

Letterguide, Inc.
Lettering equipment
2709 O St.
Lincoln, Neb. 68510

The A. Lietz Company
Drafting equipment
1224 S. Hope St.
Los Angeles, Calif. 90015

George F. Muth Co., Inc.
Art and drafting
1332 New York Avenue, N.W.
Washington, D.C. 20005

National Card, Mat & Board
   Company
4318 W. Carroll Ave.
Chicago, Ill. 60624

Paasche Airbrush Company
1909 W. Diversey Parkway
Chicago, Ill. 60614

Para-Tone, Inc.
Alphabets, patterns, pictographs
512 W. Burlington Ave.
La Grange, Ill. 60526

Prestype, Inc.
Lettering, patterns
136 W. 21st St.
New York, N.Y. 10011

Shiva Artist's Colors
Tenth and Monroe Sts.
Paducah, Ky. 42001

Heidl Slocum Company, Inc.
Drawing and lettering pens
95 Chambers St.
New York, N.Y. 10008

J. S. Staedtler, Inc.
Lettering sets, pencils, pens
P. O. Box 68
Montville, N.J. 07045

Stik-a-Letter Company
Rt. 2, Box 1400
Escondido, Calif. 92025

Strathmore Paper Company
Front St.
West Springfield, Mass. 01089

Tactype Company
Alphabets, patterns, pictographs
43 W. Sixteenth St.
New York, N.Y. 10011

Talens & Son, Inc.
Art supplies
P. O. Box 453
Union, N.J. 07083

Thayer & Chandler, Inc.
Airbrush and equipment
215 W. Ohio St.
Chicago, Ill. 60610

Varigraph Company, Inc.
Lettering instrument
Madison, Wis. 53701

VariTyper Corp.
Headliner, photographic type
11 Mt. Pleasant Ave.
E. Hanover, N.J. 07936

Venus Pen & Pencil Corp.
730 Fifth Ave.
New York, N.Y. 10019

Visual Systems Co., Inc.
Art and drafting
1154 Nineteenth St., N.W.
Washington, D.C. 20036

F. Weber Company
Art supplies
1220 Buttonwood St.
Philadelphia, Pa. 19123

Winsor & Newton, Inc.
Art supplies
881 Broadway
New York, N.Y. 10003

Wold Air Brush Company
2171 N. California
Chicago, Ill. 60647

X-Acto, Inc.
Cutting knives and blades
48–41 Van Dam St.
Long Island City, N.Y. 11101

Zip-A-Tone
Alphabets, patterns, pictographs
512 W. Burlington Ave.
La Grange, Ill. 60526

PROJECTION AND DISPLAY EQUIPMENT

American Visual Aids
Easels
21 33rd St.
Brooklyn, N.Y. 11232

Bausch & Lomb, Inc.
Overhead projectors
635 St. Paul St.
Rochester, N.Y. 14602

Bell & Howell
Audiovisual equipment
7100 McCormick
Chicago, Ill. 60645

Charles Beseler Company
Vu-Graph projectors
219 S. Eighteenth St.
East Orange, N.J. 07018

The Blackridge Company
Graph-Pak Display
Conlin Road, RFD 1
Charlton, Mass. 01507

The Brewster Corp., Dept. 41
Exhibit panels and lights
Old Lyme, Conn. 06371

Da-Lite Screen Company, Inc.
Projection screens
Rte. 15N Detroit Road
Warsaw, Ind. 46580

Eastman Kodak Company
Audiovisual techniques and
  services
343 State St.
Rochester, N.Y. 14650

Graphic Systems
Boardmaster Visual Control
925 Danville Road
Yanceyville, N.C. 27379

William Hayett
Exhibit kits
207 W. 25th St.
New York, N.Y. 10001

Keuffel & Esser Company
Projectors and graphic
  techniques
30 Speedwell Ave.
Morristown, N.J. 07960

Madison A-V Company, Inc.
Magnetic systems and accessories
62 Grand St.
New York, N.Y. 10013

Minnesota Mining & Mfg.
  Company
Overhead projectors and
  reproduction
2501 Hudson Road
St. Paul, Minn. 55119

Porta-Zibit
Exhibit kits
6511 Chillum Place, N.W.
Washington, D.C. 20012

Radiant Mfg. Corp.
Projection screens
8220 N. Austin Ave.
North Hollywood, Calif. 60053

Technamation, Inc.
Motion material kit
Eleven Sintsink Drive E.
Port Washington, N.Y. 11050

Universal Screen Company
Projection screens
7251 N. Varna Ave.
North Hollywood, Calif. 91605

Visucom Division
Technifax Division
The Plastic Coating Corp.
Overhead projection equipment
  and materials
195 Appleton St.
Holyoke, Mass. 01040

Index

WHICH CHART TO USE?
THE DATA

Radios Produced in the United States (*In thousands*)

Year	Home sets	Portable battery sets	Auto sets	Total sets	Percent automotive
1958	2,621	3,373	3,715	11,747	31.6
1959	3,145	4,128	5,555	15,622	35.6
1960	3,440	4,535	6,432	17,127	37.6
1961	3,042	5,747	5,568	17,374	32.0
1962	3,015	5,640	7,250	19,162	37.8
1963	2,496	4,614	7,947	18,281	43.5
1964	2,947	4,358	8,313	19,176	43.4
1965	3,382	6,031	10,037	24,118	41.6
1966	3,434	6,280	9,394	23,595	39.8

Source: Electronic Industries Association. (1968 Automobile Facts and Figures.)

The Line Chart
Chapter 4

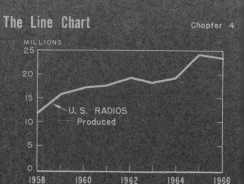

The Index Chart
Chapter 4

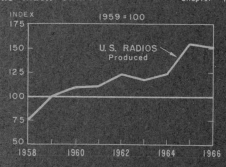

Cumulative
Chapter 4

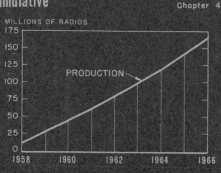

The Column Chart
Chapter 6

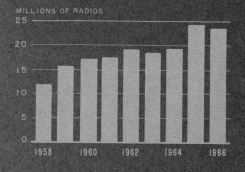

Grouped Column
Chapter 6

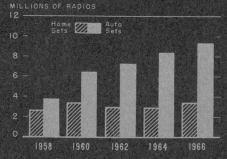

The Bar Chart
Chapter 7

Sliding Bar
Chapter 7

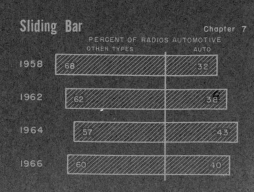